THE THIRD DOG

Also by Nigel Robinson:

The Doctor Who Quiz Book
The Second Doctor Who Quiz Book
The Doctor Who Crossword Book

THE THIRD DOCTOR WHO QUIZ BOOK

Compiled by
Nigel Robinson

TARGET

A TARGET BOOK
published by
the Paperback Division of
W.H. Allen & Co. PLC

A Target Book
Published in 1985
by the Paperback Division of
W.H. Allen & Co. PLC
44 Hill Street, London W1X 8LB

Printed and bound in Great Britain by
Anchor Brendon Ltd, Tiptree, Essex

ISBN 0 426 20212 0

CONTENTS

THE QUESTIONS

General/1

1. The Doctor has so far regenerated five times. Give the reason for each regeneration.
2. Who was Charles Crichton?
3. What use is commonly made of vintaric crystals?
4. Which of the following races has never, to the best of the Doctor's knowledge, visited Earth? Daleks, Exxilons, the Fendahl, Cybermen, the Jagaroth, the Macra.
5. Put the following adventures, all set in Mankind's future, in their correct chronological order: *Frontios*; *The Ark*; *Earthshock*; *Frontier in Space*; *The Seeds of Death*.
6. Which of the following monarchs has the Doctor never met? (a) Queen Elizabeth II; (b) King Edward VII; (c) King Richard the Lionheart; (d) King John; (e) Queen Victoria.
7. Where exactly on Space Station J7 did the second Doctor's TARDIS materialise? Where did the sixth Doctor's?
8. Name the wife of (a) Emperor Nero; (b) King Dalios; (c) the Federator of Manussa.
9. The co-ordinates of Gallifrey are ten, zero, eleven, zero, zero by zero-two from galactic zero centre. Which planet shares these co-ordinates – but to the negative value?
10. Who bought, or tried to buy (a) Earth? (b) Argolis? (c) Ribos?
11. The Master is notorious for his ability to assume a variety of convincing disguises. In which adventure did the Doctor disguise himself as (a) a milkman? (b) a German doctor? (c) a gypsy fiddler? (d) a washerwoman?
12. Which constitution prohibits vapourisation without representation?
13. Who were the two Doctors?
14. Who or what was (a) Rondal? (b) Rondel?
15. Name the daughters of the following scientists; (a) Professor Travers; (b) Edward Waterfield; (c) Professor Watkins; (d) Tremas; (e) Mr Range.

1. Why was the first Doctor in favour of Lord President Borusa receiving Rassilon's gift of immortality?
2. Who was the first person to resist the influence of the Conscience of Marinus?
3. Why was Tegana travelling with Marco Polo's party at the time of the first Doctor's visit to China?
4. How did the Celestial Toymaker prevent the Doctor from warning and helping Steven and Dodo, and force the Time Lord to play the Trilogic Game?
5. Name the bartender and chanteuse at the Last Chance Saloon.
6. Which planet visited by the Doctor once boasted of a flower forest which covered the planet in a cocoon of peace, but when the TARDIS crew arrived was a barren and almost lifeless world?
7. Which member of the TARDIS crew was sent to a Garden of Peace in Mexico?
8. Who were the 'Hollywood stars' who Morton Dill saw practising their special effects on top of the Empire State Building?
9. At Coal Hill School Susan Foreman was something of an enigma: absolutely brilliant in some subjects, she would betray a shocking ignorance in others. But she did show some outstanding skills in one particular subject, so much so that Barbara suggested that she should specialise in it. What was it?
10. The London sewers have harboured many dangers for the time-travellers throughout the years. The Cybermen made their base here and launched their invasion of London through its sewers. Magnus Greel's mutated giant rat almost killed Leela here too. What were the circumstances which caused the sewers to become infested with alligators?
11. Why did the Doctor, Ian, Barbara and Susan become minituarised in *Planet of Giants*?
12. On which planet is the sky the colour of burnt orange, and the leaves on the trees a bright silver?
13. Why did Paris seek revenge on Achilles?
14. Name the leader of the Sensorites encountered by the

TARDIS crew.

15. Who was Dako?
16. Who were Garge and Bors on Desperus?
17. Name two of the Savages encountered by the time-travellers on Jano's world.
18. Which race of creatures was guided back to the Delta of Light?
19. What was the purpose of the meeting between Napoleon and Paul Barras at the Sinking Ship – an inn on the road to Calais?
20. What important secret did Holy Joe Longford hold?

Adventures in History/1

1. Who hid in a priest hole in 1643 and was released from there in 1984?
2. Name the four sons of Pa Clanton. How did each of them meet their deaths?
3. Whose murdered body did the Doctor and Vicki discover on the road to Rome?
4. What were the circumstances which brought a peasant from the England of King John to the twentieth century?
5. What was the Doctor's 'blue engine'?
6. Who invented the radio telescope some forty years early, and through it detected a message being beamed at the Earth from Mars?
7. How did George Cranleigh die?
8. Leaving ancient Rome, the TARDIS fell under the influence of what great power?
9. Who were the Hashashins?
10. Who recited a poem about them to the TARDIS crew?
11. The first Doctor was present at the conclusion of the Trojan War. Indeed, he was directly responsible for the Fall of Troy. Which other Time Lord – unbeknown to the Doctor at that time – was also present during the Trojan Wars?
12. Name the wife and son of Ranulf Fitzwilliam.
13. Who was the Tythonian Beast?
14. Name the three servants of Yetaxa.
15. Why did Nero set fire to Rome?

16. Who did Irongron call 'toad-face'?
17. Who was Tigilinius?
18. Why had King John returned to Lord Ranulf's castle at the time of the fifth Doctor's visit to the thirteenth century?
19. Arriving in eleventh-century England, the TARDIS crew discovered many anachronisms such as a wristwatch, a record player and a flashlight. Who had brought these objects to that time?
20. The Silurians were mistakenly so named, for they do not come from Earth's Silurian period. From what geological period do they come?

The Adventures of the Second Doctor/1

1. In which adventure were the Doctor and his friends trapped in a forest of words?
2. How did the Ice Warriors intend to use their Seed Pods to make Earth's atmosphere more suitable for colonisation? How were the Seed Pods transported to Earth?
3. Why did the second Doctor 'bend' the Laws of Time in *The Five Doctors*?
4. Who was Cully?
5. Name King George's Commissioner of Prisons in the Highlands, who was encountered by the TARDIS crew.
6. Name the two students from Class 3196 in the First Grade who were chosen to be Companions of the Krotons.
7. En route to Mars, the TARDIS was dragged off-course and materialised on the Moon's surface. What power had caused this deviation in the ship's course?
8. Who was the first person Zoe met after the Time Lords returned her to the Wheel in Space?
9. Who decided to present a Strangers' Trophy every year at a Dance Festival? Why?
10. Who was Michelle Lopez?
11. Arrested for spying in the First World War war zone, what punishment was meted out to each member of the TARDIS crew?
12. Who set sail from Bristol on 4 May 1699, and was

encountered by the second Doctor?

13. Why did the second Doctor travel to Space Station J7? What was his first visit there?
14. Why were the Chameleons a faceless and sterile race?
15. How did they propose to gain new identities for themselves?
16. Which of the Doctor's enemies kept an octopus as a pet?
17. Who did the Highlanders support? Who did the Redcoats support?
18. The antique shop visited by the Doctor and Jamie in *Evil of the Daleks* had an impressive stock of brand new – and genuine – antiques. How could this have been so?
19. Where in London did the final showdown between the Doctor and the Great Intelligence take place?
20. Name 'the greatest living scientist since Leonardo' who disappeared some twenty years before the second Doctor encountered him.

The Daleks and the Thals/1

1. Who appointed himself as Davros's executioner?
2. On which planet was there to be found a 10,000-strong Dalek army?
3. What was the Power of the Daleks?
4. When the Doctor and Romana visited Skaro, they found the Daleks to be in the middle of a bitter war with the Movellans. Ninety years later that war had ended. Who won the war, and how?
5. Who destroyed two Daleks with an ultra-sonic beam of rock 'n' roll?
6. Who were Alpha, Beta and Omega?
7. Who planned to destroy the Daleks with a deadly virus and then create a new race of Daleks, obeying only his will?
8. To which planet did the Daleks travel to collect the Doctor from the trap which the Master had set?
9. What treacherous deal, unwittingly sanctioned by Susan, did the Daleks arrange with the Thals on Skaro?
10. Defeated on Skaro, Davros was put into cryogenic

suspension and taken to Earth for trial. What verdict was passed on him?

11. Name the legendary hero who came to the aid of the Thals on Spiridon.

12. Who did the Kaleds originally suspect the Doctor and Harry to be when they were captured in Section 101 of the battleground on Skaro?

13. Name three of the planets visited by the Doctor and his friends in their struggle to foil the Daleks' Master Plan.

14. The Daleks came to Skaro to seek Davros's aid in their war with the Movellans. Why did they need his help ninety years later?

15. Marc Cory had long suspected that the Daleks were embarking on some sort of evil Master Plan. The Daleks' acquisition of over seventy planets in the Ninth Galactic System, and forty in the Miros constellation, only strengthened his conviction. But what finally gave him conclusive proof that the Daleks were present in force on the planet Kembel?

16. To escape from the Dalek city on Skaro, Ian hid inside a Dalek casing; the Thal Rebec used a similar ruse to penetrate the Dalek city on Spiridon. Under what circumstances did the first Doctor hide inside a Dalek casing?

17. How did Kara plan to kill Davros on Necros?

18. How were Daleks inadvertently brought to nineteenth-century Earth by Theodore Maxtible and Edward Waterfield?

19. Name the Commander of the Dalek troopers after the creatures' massive defeat at the hands of the Movellans.

20. How long had the Daleks ruled the Earth before the third Doctor ended their evil reign?

The Adventures of the Third Doctor/1

1. Who was the emissary of the gods who arrived in Ancient Atlantis in a computer bank?

2. Where was the Devil's Hump to be found?

16

3. During the Doctor's first few days of exile to Earth, many interesting facts were learnt about his physical make-up, including the fact that he was able to put himself into a coma. Why did the Doctor put himself into a coma?

4. The explosion which destroyed Auderley House and killed the foreign diplomats, whose deaths directly led to the Third World War, left no trace of radiation. Why?

5. Name the hermaphrodite hexapod twice encountered by the Doctor.

6. Which was the first alien planet to be visited by the Doctor during his exile?

7. Name the eminent scientist who spent some little time at Athens University before coming to England to conduct a series of experiments in time.

8. Who was Barnham at Stangmoor Prison?

9. What was the crowning – and final – triumph of the Exxilon race?

10. Which ship en route to Bombay mysteriously disappeared from the Indian Ocean on 4 June 1926?

11. Who was Professor Dale?

12. The Silurians initially intended to wipe out Earth's population by infecting Major Baker with a deadly plague. For what use was the 'plague' originally developed millions of years ago?

13. Upon returning to Earth, the three astronauts of the Mars Probe Seven flight were found to be emitting 2 million rads of radiation. How could this be?

14. Who was Professor Kettering? How did he die, apparently from drowning in a perfectly dry room?

15. Stahlman was the leader and *de facto* head of Project Inferno. Who was the project's executive director?

16. Name the sole prisoner of Governor George Trenchard.

17. What was the main difference between the surface and subterranean Exxilons?

18. Landing in Covent Garden underground station the second Doctor and his friends were soon afterwards attacked by the Yeti. What manner of monster attacked the third Doctor at Westminster underground station?

19. In which adventure did the Doctor find himself having

to spend the night in a waxworks?
20. 'Klokleda partha mennin klatch; araan, araan, aroon.'
    Translate.

Companions of the Doctor/1

1. Why did Tegan finally leave the Doctor?
2. When the second Doctor arrived on Dastari's space
   station, Shockeye offered to buy Jamie from the Time
   Lord. But which of the Doctor's companions was
   actually sold – for 10,000 sesterces?
3. Which of the Doctor's companions admitted taking an
   'O' Level in science – but not necessarily passing it?
4. After his third regeneration the Doctor mistook which
   of his companions for Alexander the Great?
5. In which adventure was Peri almost transmogrified
   into a human-bird creature?
6. As they left Mexico, the Doctor remarked to Barbara
   that although she had failed to change history, she had
   at least helped one man. Who was he?
7. Which of the following companions of the Doctor is the
   odd one out? Katarina; Sara Kingdom; Adric; Jamie.
8. What technological marvel did Jamie once describe as
   'twenty castles in the sky'?
9. Where was Peri planning to travel to before she met the
   Doctor and Turlough and embarked on even stranger
   adventures?
10. What was Leela's blasphemy? What judgement did the
    Sevateem pass on her?
11. Sarah Jane has been one of the Doctor's longest serving
    companions and in her travels met all manner of alien
    life forms. Which of the following creatures have never
    been encountered by the young journalist? Daleks;
    Cybermen; Yeti; Sontarans; Sea Devils; Ice Warriors.
12. After the Sontaran attack on Space Station J7 where
    did Jamie take refuge?
13. Which of the Doctor's companions have been school-
    teachers?
14. When did the Doctor first make the acquaintance of
    Sergeant Benton of UNIT?

15. Which of the Doctor's companions was taken over by a spider on (a) Metebelis Three? (b) Alzarius?

The Adventures of the Fourth Doctor/1

1. Who destroyed Phaester Osiris?
2. At the time of the Doctor and Sarah Jane's visit to Karn, the Sacred Flame of Life was apparently dying. However at the Sisters' ceremonies the Flame burned as brightly as ever. Why?
3. What happened to the Tharils on the Day of the Feast?
4. Who swallowed the symbol of power, killed his high priest and grew to enormous size?
5. Who posed as an executive of the Magellanic Mining Corporation in pursuance of his own greedy gain?
6. Which member of the TARDIS crew has visited Crinoth?
7. What was to be found on Asteroid K4067? Why did Leela take the Doctor there?
8. What was Neophobos?
9. Why were the Wirrn forced to leave their breeding colonies in Andromeda?
10. Eldrad's true form was of a large, heavy crystalline monster. Why did he then initially assume the form of a beautiful female alien?
11. What exactly was the Power Complex on Skonnos?
12. Who was Marn?
13. According to ancient Taran law, what would happen if the heir apparent to the Taran throne missed the appointed hour of his coronation?
14. How does an Argolin die?
15. Who mined for zelanite and lucanol?
16. What was to be found inside the Biomagnetron on Oseidon?
17. Which of the Doctor's foes became 'a fly caught by honey'?
18. What is so peculiar about the interior decorative style of the old Thesaurian Empire?
19. On which planet did the Doctor and Romana discover the grave of a Kantrian, buried far away from the

tropical planet on which he was born?

20. The only effective way to kill a Great Vampire was to drive a stake through its heart. This was not merely superstition – there were very practical reasons for doing so. What were they?

The Adventures of the Fifth Doctor/1

1. Who was Sharaz Jek?
2. Name the Lord of the Manor at Little Hodcombe. Who was his right-hand man?
3. How did the Doctor escape Gallifrey without Omega's knowledge during the solar engineer's second attempt to enter the universe of matter?
4. Name the sole prisoner of the prison space station visited by the Doctor, Tegan and Turlough. What was to happen to this prisoner in the event of the station being boarded by enemy forces?
5. To escape the final destruction of Earth, mankind emigrated en masse. Many settled on the planet Refusis and were encountered by the first Doctor. On which planet did the fifth Doctor meet a similar group of colonists?
6. Name all the aliens to be found in the Death Zone on Gallifrey at the time of Borusa's resumption of the Game.
7. Who brought the TARDIS to Sarn?
8. What do an agrarian commissioner on Vardon, a tax inspector on Derveg, and a solicitor in Chancery Lane have in common?
9. Who sang 'in praise of total war'?
10. What is the more common name of Planet G139901Kb in the Scrampus System?
11. Which planet once circled the star Inokshi?
12. What was Sentinel Six?
13. What was the Magma Beast?
14. List all of Kamelion's assumed forms before his destruction at the hands of the Doctor.
15. What was the Malus?
16. What was the first recorded appearance of the Malus?

17. How did the Doctor defeat the Gravis on Frontios? To which planet did the Time Lord exile him?
18. Name the Commander of the Federation Forces on Androzani Minor.
19. How did Professor Hayter of Darlington University 'die'?
20. The Master, making use of Adric's mathematical abilities, created Castrovalva. Who destroyed it?

The Master

1. With which other Gallifreyan did the Master enter into an uneasy alliance on nineteenth-century Earth?
2. Why did the Master come to Sarn?
3. After the Master had escaped UNIT after the Sea Devil affair, how did the Doctor plan to track the evil Time Lord down?
4. Who held the whole genius of night at his command?
5. Sending the Master into the Death Zone to rescue the Doctor, what did the High Council give the evil Time Lord to present to the Doctor as a gesture of good faith?
6. How did the Master journey to Logopolis?
7. Why did the Master find it extremely difficult to control the power of the Xeraphin?
8. Why did the Doctor enter into an uneasy alliance with his enemy on Logopolis?
9. The Master and the Doctor are about the same age, and indeed attended the Academy together. Why did the Master reach the end of his cycle of twelve regenerations and his thirteenth body, when the Doctor was only in his fourth incarnation?
10. How did the Master dispose of the Doctor's TARDIS when the Time Lords met on nineteenth-century Earth?
11. What bizarre disguise did the Master briefly assume on nineteenth-century Earth?
12. Why had the Master come to Earth at that particular point in its history?
13. Under what circumstances did the Doctor engage in a sword fight with the Master?

14. How did the Master hide his enemy's TARDIS on Traken?
15. Who was the Master's unwilling slave on Sarn?

The Time Lords/1

1. Who was the Deadly Assassin?
2. Which of the following Gallifreyans was not at the Time Lord Academy at the same time as the Doctor? The Master; Romana; Drax; Borusa; Runcible.
3. Who is Gold Usher?
4. To where did Spandrell order the Doctor's TARDIS to be transduced after it had materialised in the Cloisters of the Capitol on Gallifrey?
5. What is the role of the Castellan on Gallifrey?
6. A Staatenheim Remote Control is a remarkable device enabling a Time Lord to control his TARDIS by remote control. Which two Time Lords have been seen to use such a device?
7. Who was Professor Edgeworth?
8. Like the Master, the Rani was also an exiled Time Lord. Why was she exiled from Gallifrey?
9. Which Time Lord possessed a Mark IV TARDIS which had been constructed some fifty years after the Doctor's own?
10. What was the Harp of Rassilon?
11. Which member of the High Council was falsely accused of using the Time Scoop to bring the Doctor and his other selves and companions into the Death Zone on Gallifrey?
12. What directive found in the Record of Rassilon did the great Time Lord give to all his fellows?
13. Arriving on Castrovalva, the Doctor picked a stalk of celery and attached it to his buttonhole, rather curiously proclaiming it to be a sign of civilisation. What significance does celery have for Gallifreyans?
14. Name the two marriage alliances between Earth and Gallifrey.
15. How did the Master persuade the Rani to ally herself with him?

1. What was the Timelash?
2. What is the official colour of mourning on Necros?
3. Arriving on Earth in nineteenth-century England with Peri the Doctor detected a disturbance in the time continuum. What was causing it?
4. Why was Jondar sentenced to execution on Varos? What was to be his manner of execution?
5. Name the two sons of Professor Sylvest? What was so unusual about them?
6. Who was Chessene?
7. How did she die?
8. Emerging from a Kontron Tunnel, the TARDIS console room was briefly invaded by a 'phantom'. Who was the 'phantom'?
9. Which planet in the constellation of Cetes has been visited by the Doctor and Peri?
10. Who was Lieutenant Hugo Lang?
11. What was to be found in the catacombs of Necros?
12. What is a gumblejack?
13. What are the peculiar properties of Mustakozene 80?
14. Where did the TARDIS materialise when the Doctor attempted to take Peri to Kew Gardens? Why did it materialise in this location?
15. The Varosians had a most unusual, but highly effective, method of registering their disapproval of their Governor. What was it?
16. Jaconda was once a green and beautiful planet. What had caused the terrible devastation witnessed by the Doctor and Peri when the TARDIS brought them to that planet?
17. Who attempted to pay for a gourmet meal with a twenty-narg note?
18. In the immediate wake of his fifth regeneration, and wracked with guilt at his attempted murder of Peri, the Doctor decided to become a hermit and atone for his crimes in the most desolate place in the Universe. Where did he travel to?
19. Name the Knight of the Grand Order of Oberon whom the Doctor met on Necros. Why had the knight come

to that planet?
20. Who was Megelen?

The Adventures of the First Doctor/2

1. Who dwelt in the Valley of Caves?
2. After his escape from Gallifrey, who was the first member of his own race whom the Doctor encountered?
3. Marco Polo intended to present Kublai Khan with a gift so magnificent that he hoped that Khan would give him permission to return to his home of Venice which he had left in 1271. What was this gift?
4. Who were the 'servants without voice'?
5. In which adventure did the TARDIS materialise inside a South American tomb?
6. Vicki left Earth in 2493 with her father after her mother's death. Where were they heading?
7. Who were John Smith and the Common Men?
8. How did the intelligent plants on Esto communicate with each other?
9. What device did the Drahvins use to immobilise a Chumbley on the doomed planet in Galaxy Four?
10. Who claimed he could make the brave man braver, the wise man wiser, the strong man stronger and the beautiful girl even more beautiful? And what were the horrifying consequences of doing so?
11. Arriving in twentieth-century London, the first Doctor and his friends were obliged to split up, Ian and the Doctor leaving Barbara and Susan behind. Why?
12. Which of the Doctor's companions had already by the age of ten gained certificates in medicine, physics and chemistry?
13. What deal did the Doctor reach with Ixta, the Aztecs' Chosen Warrior?
14. Name the two other members of Marc Cory's team on Kembel.
15. Who was given the sobriquet 'Snake Eyes'?
16. Name three of the games played by the TARDIS crew in the Celestial Toymaker's domain.
17. What is an Atmospheric Density Jacket? On which

planet did the Doctor and Ian use them?

18. There was initially a great deal of animosity between the Doctor and Ian and Barbara. What – in the Doctor's own words – finally made companions of them all?

19. Where did the Aridians and the Mire Beasts live before their home planet and its two suns moved closer together?

20. Who were armed with heat-prods?

Adventures in History/2

1. Name the genius encountered by the Doctor and Peri who changed the course of Earth's history.

2. Where was the Terileptil base in the London of 1666 situated? How did the Doctor pinpoint its location?

3. How did the second Doctor and his friends gain the trust of Colin McLaren and his company?

4. What was the Black Orchid?

5. At whose villa on the outskirts of Rome did the first Doctor, Ian, Barbara and Vicki stay in AD 64?

6. Who warned the Doctor to beware the Eye of the Dragon? What was the Eye of the Dragon?

7. How did the dentist of Tombstone propose to anaesthetise the Doctor prior to extracting the Time Lord's tooth?

8. Who massacred Sir John and his family in his manor house in seventeenth-century England?

9. Who was Robespierre?

10. Why was George Cranleigh so interested in Nyssa?

11. Which cult, which had supposedly died out in the third century, was very much alive when the Doctor visited sixteenth-century Italy?

12. Name the King encountered by the Doctor and Jo who had lived for more than five hundred years.

13. Attacked by a group of bandits in the secret service of Tegana, what ruse did the TARDIS crew and Marco Polo use to frighten them away?

14. Which 'old friend' did the Doctor lose in 1666?

15. How did the Doctor become engaged to the Aztec lady, Cameca?

16. How did Polly engineer her and Ben's escape from a Cornish prison in the seventeenth century?
17. Which particular part of English history were Sir George Hutchinson's war games recreating?
18. Why was it necessary for him to recreate this piece of history?
19. In which circumstances did the Doctor gain the sacred tooth of Buddha and the total animal produce of Burma?
20. What drew the TARDIS off-course and took it to the England of 1911 after the Doctor and Sarah Jane had left Zeta Minor?

The Adventures of the Second Doctor/2

1. Name the two 'gentlemen of the old school' who went on a gourmet tour of Seville.
2. What manner of creature did the second Doctor and the Brigadier meet in the tunnels underneath the Dark Tower?
3. Which of the Doctor's foes hailed from Mérida in Yucatan?
4. Which superhero became Zoe's slave?
5. Whose decision was it to bring the second and third Doctors together in *The Three Doctors*?
6. How did Zoe's photographic memory and petiteness enable herself and her friends to escape from their cell on Gallifrey?
7. Which of the following are not Gonds? Beta; Axus; Teel; Vana; Kando.
8. The Island of Death was to be found in the southern hemisphere of Dulkis. Why did the Dominators land there?
9. What enabled the Chameleons to keep a stable hold on the human forms they had assumed?
10. What was the time-travellers' first view of a Macra?
11. How did Varga release his fellow warriors from the ice?
12. Name the T-Mat Technical Co-ordinator.
13. Whose rally cry was *Creag an tuire*?
14. Who attempted to sacrifice the TARDIS crew at the

Vernal Equinox?

15. Name Tobias Vaughn's sadistic right-hand man.
16. Faced with a charging unicorn in the Land of Fiction, how did the Doctor save himself and his companions?
17. After their adventure in the Land of Fiction, where did the TARDIS next take the time-travellers?
18. Who were the Fish People?
19. Where had the Doctor's old friend, Professor Travers, and his daughter, Anne Travers, gone to at the time of the Cybermen's invasion of London?
20. Which member of the crew of the Wheel in Space was detailed to keep a watch on Jamie?

Companions of the Doctor/2

1. Why did the Doctor leave Susan? When did they next meet?
2. When the Doctor first met her Sarah Jane was posing as Lavinia Smith, her aunt and a noted virologist. How did the Doctor see through her disguise?
3. What was Turlough's first name and rank?
4. Who longed to eat Peri and Jamie?
5. There have been three models of K9. Why was each one manufactured?
6. The Doctor has tried, rather unsuccessfully, to persuade Peri of the delights of taking a holiday in the Eye of Orion. Which of his companions has he taken there?
7. Which of the Doctor's companions was placed under the personal protection of which member of English royalty?
8. How did Adric's brother die? How did Sara Kingdom's?
9. Why did the Swampies decide to sacrifice Romana to Kroll?
10. Jo Grant was once proposed to by the King of Peladon; the Duke Giuliano of San Martino had more than a platonic interest in Sarah Jane Smith. Peri, however, has not been so lucky in affairs of the heart. Name the two men who have desired the Doctor's young American companion as a bride.
11. Which of the Doctor's companions almost became a

second Scheherezade?

12. The Doctor, Ian, Barbara and Vicki assumed that Steven Taylor had died in the conflagration which engulfed the Mechonoid city. How did he survive?

13. In *Earthshock* Adric expressed a desire to return to his own people on Terradon. To do this would have meant negotiating a passage through the CVE and into E-space. Adric was sure he could do this, with or without the Doctor's help. Who would he have turned to help for once in E-Space?

14. Upon receiving the summons to Gallifrey the fourth Doctor was forced to leave Sarah Jane behind on Earth. When did Sarah finally visit the planet of the Time Lords?

15. What was the ruse used by Peri to enter the Doña Arana's hacienda, thereby causing a diversion enabling the Doctor and Jamie to slip in unnoticed?

The Cybermen/1

1. Earth has always been a much-valued prize for the Cybermen because of its immense mineral wealth. But what other vital 'commodity' is the planet particularly rich in?

2. What was 'Cocktail Polly'?

3. What were the Cyber Androids, encountered by Lieutenant Scott and his party, protecting?

4. The Cybermen have often used human traitors in their schemes. Which one of them was partially turned into a Cyberman?

5. How did the Master succeed in destroying his Cybermen 'allies' on Gallifrey?

6. Who was Talon?

7. How did the second Doctor finally succeed in destroying the Cybership in *The Wheel in Space*?

8. Place the following Cyberman adventures in their correct chronological order in the history of Earth: *The Moonbase*; *Attack of the Cybermen*; *The Tenth Planet*; *Earthshock*.

9. Who were the original inhabitants of Telos?

10. Name all the adventures in which the Cybermats have appeared.
11. The use of Cyberbombs were banned by which military convention?
12. Name three members of the Moonbase personnel.
13. How many years had the Cybermen collaborated with Tobias Vaughn in their planned invasion of Earth?
14. Captain Briggs's freighter experienced several inexplicable power losses on its way to Earth. What was the reason for them?
15. On which planet did the Cybermen intend to visit their revenge?

The Adventures of the Third Doctor/2

1. What is the most perfect killing machine ever invented? Where did the third Doctor meet one?
2. Name the Greek Titan who ate his own children.
3. What were the reasons for the Doctor's presence at Project Inferno?
4. Who was Jane Blythe?
5. Name the leader of the Earth opposition party in 2540.
6. Faced with the failure of his plans, how did Eckersley attempt to procure for himself a safe escape from Peladon?
7. After the Doctor discovered a cure to their plague, the Silurians planned to kill the Humans by destroying the Van Allen Belt. How did they intend to put this plan into operation, and how would it have destroyed mankind?
8. The third Doctor equipped Bessie with an anti-theft device. What effect did it have on would-be thieves, and in which adventure was it put to use?
9. What lay beyond the peculiar octagonal plate to be found on board the *SS Bernice*?
10. How was the war between the Galactic Federation and Galaxy Five brought to a successful conclusion?
11. On which planet was the TARDIS completely cocooned in a sponge-like substance which was so effective that the Doctor was unable to open the doors and leave the

time-machine?

12. Under which circumstances was a UNIT force attacked by a knight in armour, a group of Roundheads and a V1 bomber?

13. Who reminded Jo Grant of a younger version of the Doctor?

14. Throughout history and legend mankind has been in awe of, and feared, powerful horned beasts. What was the factual basis behind this legend?

15. Name the doctor who cared for the third Doctor at Ashbridge Cottage Hospital immediately after the Time Lord's second regeneration.

16. How did the Daleks hope to track down the guerillas who had journeyed through time in an attempt to stop the Third World War?

17. Why was Winser of the Nuton Centre so interested in acquiring axonite?

18. Exactly how did the Keller Machine reform hardened criminals?

19. Name the Most Venerable Priest of Poseidon and King of the Ten Kings.

20. Who was Petra Williams?

The Daleks and the Thals/2

1. On which planet did the Daleks seek their destiny?
2. Who was Stien?
3. Alerted of the presence of their creator on Necros, why did the Daleks come to arrest Davros?
4. Davros offered immortality to Jobel. What manner of eternal life did Davros have in mind?
5. Why was Edward Waterfield forced to co-operate with the Daleks?
6. On the run from the Daleks, where did Dortmun, Barbara and Jenny decided to flee to? Why?
7. On which planet did the Daleks temporarily lose their power to kill?
8. Who was Gerrill?
9. Using mirrors, the Thals were able to reflect light onto the Dalek City's sensors, thereby blinding the City. How

then did the Daleks track down and capture the Doctor and Susan in Section 15 of the city wall?

10. What did the Daleks from Skaro intend to do with Davros's Daleks on Necros?

11. Exactly how were the Daleks destroyed during their first invasion of Earth?

12. When they met again on Necros, what ultimate fate did Davros intend to visit upon the Doctor?

13. Where did the Daleks hide the cylinders containing samples of the deadly Movellan virus? Why?

14. Name the two known instances in which the Daleks have employed the services of the Ogrons.

15. Which planet developed a fleet of rockets which were totally resistant to Dalek firepower?

16. Which TARDIS crewmember was the first to meet a Dalek?

17. At the time of the Doctor and Romana's visit to Skaro, the planet's surface was suffering from periodic explosions. Why?

18, How did Davros, released from cryogenic suspension, obtain two Daleks, which he promptly reconditioned to obey only his will?

19. Who betrayed Barbara and Jenny to the Daleks in Bedfordshire?

20. Who was Kisten?

The Adventures of the Fourth Doctor/2

1. Who showed the Doctor a vision of the Tharil Empire at its height?

2. Who had been sent off to explore the solar system in XK5? What happened to him?

3. What were the Screens of Zolfa-Thura?

4. Who had to pay the Cost of the Golden Death?

5. What was the great source of protein to be found on Delta Three?

6. Name (a) the Prime Unit; (b) the first Med Tech; (c) the first Tech of the Ark in Space.

7. Who were Veldan and Jall?

8. How exactly does a Krynoid become the dominant life

form on a planet?
9. Who held Xoanan captive in the Place of Land?
10. Who was the King of Nothing?
11. How did Meglos steal the Dodecahedron on Tigella?
12. What was to be found at the Place of Death on Chloris?
13. How many Megropolises were established on Pluto at the time of the Doctor's visit?
14. Why did the Doctor pilot the TARDIS to Zeta Minor?
15. One particular resident of Hillview Road, South Croydon had a most peculiar pet. What was it?
16. Why did Garron and Unstoffe plant a large chunk of jethryk in the relic cabinet containing the crown jewels of Ribos?
17. A precorded message was sent from Mars to Earth in 1911, warning the Humans to beware Sutekh. What occasioned this transmission?
18. Which race of aliens was behind the Android Invasion?
19. Who were Officers Fisk and Costa?
20. Who was the Time Lord of the first rank whom the Doctor – a mere nobody – challenged to a mental duel?

The Adventures of the Fifth Doctor/2

1. What manner of creatures are the Tractators?
2. Which race of aliens, although able to breathe the Earth's atmosphere, thrived on Soliton Gas?
3. What is a Synch-Op? Name the Synch-Op encountered by the fifth Doctor.
4. Who went walkabout to the Time of the Dreaming?
5. Who was Jane Hampden?
6. Name the Chairman of the Sirius Conglomerate. Who succeeded him?
7. Who freed the Garm from the slavery of the Vanir?
8. Why did Hugh Fitzwilliam bear such ill will towards the Doctor?
9. Who was Icthar?
10. What did Enlightenment regard as the 'exchange of two fantasies'?
11. In the event of a native life form becoming hostile, what was the standard procedure advocated by the manual

which was followed by Sanders on Deva Loka?
12. Who was offered fear in a handful of dust?
13. How old was the Earth colony on Frontios?
14. Who was the Chosen One of the people of Sarn?
15. The Elixir of Life on Karn could prolong human life indefinitely. What substance found by the Doctor and Peri could also prolong human life beyond its natural extent?
16. In which star system can the planet Hakol be found?
17. How did the fifth Doctor locate Omega's base on Earth?
18. Who played Russian Roulette with the TARDIS, and why?
19. Who was Mansell?
20. Sir Reginald Styles was the influential diplomat whom guerillas from the twenty-second century attempted to assassinate, believing him to be responsible for the war which made possible the Daleks' successful invasion of Earth. But who was the Styles whom Turlough met in the far future?

The Time Lords/2

1. What is the Rassilon Imprimature?
2. What were the Black Scrolls of Rassilon?
3. Omega was defeated for the first time when the second Doctor's recorder, made of matter, was introduced into Omega's world of anti-matter. How did the Doctor defeat Omega in Amsterdam?
4. What gift did Rassilon grant to those who placed his Ring upon their finger?
5. How did the Doctor dispose of the Master and the Rani on nineteenth-century Earth?
6. Mawdryn and his fellow scientists robbed the Time Lords of the secret of bodily regeneration – with disastrous results. To which race did the Gallifreyans willingly impart this knowledge?
7. An old Gallifreyan nursery rhyme says: 'Who unto Rassilon's Tower would go, must choose – Above, Between, Below.' This referred to the three known entrances to the Dark Tower. Which Doctor, accom-

panied by which companion, took which entrance?

8. Why was Amsterdam particularly suitable in Omega's plans to enter the Universe of Matter?

9. Which arch-enemy of the Doctor was actually persuaded to help him on Gallifrey?

10. When the first Doctor regenerated, his successor implied that without the help of the TARDIS he could not survive. Indeed, after his fourth regeneration the fifth Doctor headed straight for the time-machine's Zero Room. Name the other instance in which the Doctor has regenrated *inside* the TARDIS.

11. How did the Time Lords hope to stop the Cybermen's plan to change the course of history and, in so doing, ensured the continued stability of the web of time?

12. Why were the Time Lords so concerned about the time-travel experiments of Kartz and Reimer?

13. With which other Time Lord did the Doctor share fond memories of a night of drinking by a fountain? What happened to him?

14. What particular place of importance do the Prydonians hold in Gallifreyan history?

15. Rassilon was the greatest of the Time Lords who died many years before the Doctor first left Gallifrey. However his mind lived on in the Matrix. When did the Doctor encounter the spirit of Rassilon?

The Adventures of the Sixth Doctor/2

1. Name the neighbouring planet of Karfel. Why did that planet declare war on Karfel?

2. Who was Professor Arthur Stengos?

3. Name the leader of the Ninth Sontaran Battle Group encountered by the Doctor and his friends.

4. What danger awaited the Doctor in Redfern Dell?

5. On which planet did the Doctor and Peri star in their own 'video nasty'?

6. Who was Drak?

7. On which planet did the Doctor discover a memorial to his own death?

8. Who did Oscar Botcherby believe the sixth Doctor,

Peri and Jamie to be?

9. What course of events was the inspiration for the novels, *The War of the Worlds*, *The Island of Doctor Moreau*, *The Invisible Man* and *The Time Machine*?
10. Who was the leader of the giant gastropods?
11. What was the purpose of Space Station J7?
12. Who were Bates and Stratton? Why were they so anxious to infiltrate Cyber Control on Telos, and how did they attempt to do so?
13. After leaving Jaconda, the Doctor and Peri materialised in a deserted London scrapyard in 1985. What was so special about this scrapyard?
14. Name the Time Lord who became ruler of Miasimia Goria.
15. Who were Natasha and Grigory?
16. Where did the Doctor propose to take Peri for a holiday before the TARDIS was caught up in a Kontron Tunnel?
17. Who was Dastari?
18. What are the Morlox?
19. During her stay on Necros Peri became particularly friendly with the planet's DJ. What particular service did he perform on that planet?
20. The sixth Doctor believed he had destroyed the Borad by using a Kontron Crystal which absorbed and reflected upon the megalomaniac the energies of his own time acceleration beam. Nevertheless, the Borad returned from the dead to claim Peri. How was this possible?

The Adventures of the First Doctor/3

1. Where exactly on Vortis was the Animus situated? Why?
2. Who were armed with light guns?
3. On which planet, visited by all six Doctors, can there be found an area known as Central City?
4. What deadly trap awaited the first Doctor and Tegan immediately on entering the Dark Tower?
5. Which computer correctly deduced the meaning of the word TARDIS?

6. What did the Monoids' duties consist of during the Doctor's first visit to the Space Ark?

7. Who was Carol Richmond?

8. The Doctor persuaded Vicki to join the TARDIS crew, promising her great adventures. Where did her first journey take her?

9. Which planet lay three light years away from Morok and was conquered by the forces of that planet?

10. During their travels with the Doctor, Ian and Barbara encountered many strange species, among them the Zarbi – large, ant-like creatures who lived on Vortis. But in which adventure did the schoolteachers come across a giant earthworm and a giant fly?

11. Who searched the Doctor's mind for the knowledge that would enable it to take away from Man his mastery of space?

12. After the take-off of the Rills' ship from the doomed planet in Galaxy Four, Maaga made one last desperate attempt to escape the planet's destruction. What was it?

13. Name the two doctors present in Tombstone at the time of the Shoot-Out at the OK Corral.

14. Who were the 'six deadly sisters, seven for choice'?

15. Which race encountered by the first Doctor is particularly sensitive to noise?

16. Whose son was sent up in the *Zeus V* rocket to rescue the crew of *Zeus IV*?

17. Who was Zombo?

18. The TARDIS crew attempted to alert one Mrs Hilda Rowse of the evil schemes of Forester. Who was Mrs Rowse and why were the time-travellers unable to convey their warning to her?

19. The power of the TARDIS is contained underneath its central console. What piece of equipment holds this energy in check, and indicates the amount of power being channelled through?

20. What was the Pwodarauk?

Adventures in History/3

1. Who was (a) Malec Ric? (b) Malec el Adil?

2. Name two of the children of King Priam of Troy.
3. Who was the 'servant of Sutekh'?
4. Who was the Assassin at Peking?
5. Who killed him?
6. What was the cause of the Trojan War? How did it end?
7. An ancient Egyptian scroll in the possession of Count Scarlioni depicted a grotesque one-eyed humanoid figure. What was it?
8. How did Marco Polo ensure that the Doctor and his companions would not escape in their 'flying caravan'?
9. Although on familiar terms with many of the most famous characters of history – or so he claims! – the Doctor has twice narrowly avoided meeting Leonardo da Vinci. Which Time Lord has claimed to have met this great man?
10. Who was the first Human in the history of the world to witness the materialisation of the TARDIS in his own time zone?
11. Where were the Saracens encountered by Ian and Barbara encamped?
12. What in reality were the mummies which pursued the Doctor and Sarah Jane in 1911?
13. Who were the Luddites?
14. How did King John and Sir Gilles Estram ensure Lord Ranulf's continued good behaviour towards his sovereign?
15. Who brought Mandragora to Earth in the late fifteenth-century?
16. Who was the Rider from Shang-Tu?
17. 'Deadman's secret key' was 'Smallbeer, Ringwood, Gurney'. The latter three names referred to tombstones in the graveyard where the treasure of Captain Avery was to be found in seventeenth-century Cornwall. But who was Tim Deadman?
18. Who claimed to have helped Shakespeare to write *Hamlet*?
19. What did the Doctor leave Richard Mace as a keepsake?
20. Who was Charles Preslin?

1. Who brought a Yeti back to London with him from Tibet?
2. How was Gia Kelly responsible for the defeat of the Ice Warriors' invasion fleet?
3. In which adventure did the TARDIS materialise on Space Beacon Alpha-Four? What happened to this beacon?
4. How did the second Doctor realise that the Jamie and Zoe he saw in the Dark Tower on Gallifrey were not real?
5. The Androgums are a race of beings who live only for their instincts. Name the two Androgums encountered by the Doctor.
6. Who was Julius Silverstein?
7. Who was Ola?
8. Which race attempted to power their space fleet through 'negative mass flux absorbtion'?
9. Jamie and Victoria both successfully gained the confidence of Salamander. In what capacity was each employed by the South American dictator?
10. How was the second Doctor transformed into an Androgum?
11. How did the Brigadier learn of the Doctor and Jamie's presence on Earth at the time of the Cybermen invasion?
12. Pursued by General Hermack's Minnows, how did Milo Clancey confound his pursuers' tracking devices?
13. What was the ISC? Name its commander at the time of the Doctor's involvement with the Space Pirates.
14. Zoe once described the Doctor as being almost as clever as she was. However, he did score higher marks than her on the Krotons' teaching test. How did he do this?
15. Which of the Doctor's companions disguised herself as an orange seller in Inverness?
16. How did Jamie scale the castle wall of the Master of the Land of Fiction?
17. Of the two Dominators who landed on Dulkis, which one was the Navigator?
18. In whose house near Canterbury in 1866 were the

Doctor and Jamie imprisoned?

19. His evil schemes thwarted, how did Maurice Caven plan to make his escape and at the same time destroy the Doctor and his friends?

20. Who did the Doctor attempt to pass off as Bonnie Prince Charlie?

Behind the Scenes/1

1. The very first episode of *Doctor Who* was scheduled for broadcast at 5.15 pm on Saturday, 23 November 1963. Why was it delayed by ten minutes?

2. Who wrote the script which introduced (a) the Master? (b) Borusa? (c) the Rani?

3. Who produced the following *Doctor Who* stories? (a) *Robot*; (b) *The Daleks' Master Plan*; (c) *The Pirate Planet*; (d) *The Leisure Hive*; (e) *The Abominable Snowmen*; (f) *The Dominators*; (g) *Spearhead From Space*; (h) *The Space Museum*; (i) *Pyramids of Mars*.

4. The title sequence of *Doctor Who*, showing the Doctor's face, is now quite familiar. What was the first story to feature such a title sequence?

5. In which adventure did the sixth Doctor make his appearance?

6. Who was the scientific advisor to *Doctor Who* during the mid-sixties?

7. Which British actor, famous for his roles in the *Carry On* films, and now a successful Broadway star, was at one time considered for the role of which Doctor?

8. Name the two actors to have played the part of Jamie McCrimmon.

9. Who was the art critic who was stunned by the exquisite beauty of a dematerialising TARDIS, and later appeared in a *Doctor Who* story as an enemy of Davros?

10. Match the following episode titles with the overall title of the story to which they belong:

Golden Death	*The Chase*
Death of a Spy	*The Celestial Toymaker*
A Land of Fear	*The Myth Makers*

Inferno	*The Daleks' Master Plan*
The Hall of Dolls	*The Romans*
The Death of Time	*The Reign of Terror*

11. Name Colin Baker's two roles in *Doctor Who*.
12. Many *Doctor Who* stories have had different working titles to the ones which were eventually transmitted. Which stories were at one time known by the following titles: (a) *The Vampire Mutations*; (b) *The Destructors*: (c) *The Planet That Slept*; (d) *Sentinel*; (e) *Warhead*; (f) *The Wasting*; (g) *Genesis of Terror*.
13. Who has been the longest-serving producer of *Doctor Who*?
14. Which actor to have played the Doctor has co-starred with all but one of his successors or predecessors?
15. Which *Doctor Who* story was previewed the previous week by a short clip of the Doctor addressing the show's audience and warning the viewers of the perils to come?
16. Who has put his name to more *Doctor Who* scripts than anyone else, and has written for every Doctor save William Hartnell?
17. What was *The Space Trap*?
18. Who played the role of Johnny Ringo in *The Gunfighters*? Which more important part did he play in *Doctor Who* many years later?
19. Which classic stories were repeated in *The Five Faces of Doctor Who* season, which was broadcast in the latter part of 1981?
20. What significant contribution to *Doctor Who* did Sydney Newman and Donald Wilson make?

The Cybermen/2

1. Name the Cyber Planet.
2. How did the Cybermen who had invaded space station W3 intend to alter its atmosphere so as to destroy the Wheel's entire crew?
3. Who entered the London sewers to take photographs of

Cybermen?

4. The Cybermen introduced a 'plague' on the Moonbase in 2070. They also introduced a similar virus among the personnel of Space Beacon Nerva. How exactly does this virus affect Humans?

5. Over the years the outward appearance of the Cybermen has drastically altered as the creatures constantly improve and modify their bodies. Give the two known uses of the aperture set at the top of a Cyberman's 'helmet'.

6. Upon arriving on Telos, who did Professor Parry's team believe the Doctor, Jamie and Victoria to be?

7. After taking over the Snowcap Ice Base, how did the Cybermen propose to 'save' the Base's personnel?

8. Why was Tobias Vaughn so interested in the Doctor?

9. What was the Glitter Gun?

10. Where exactly did the Cybermen hide themselves in Briggs's freighter?

11. Name the mercenary who worked for the Daleks and who appeared to the Doctor to be also working for the Cybermen.

12. What was the exact function of Nerva at the time of the Cybermen's invasion?

13. Why did the Cybermen go into hibernation on Telos? And why did they establish their tombs on that planet?

14. How exactly did the Gravitron influence the Earth's weather?

15. How long had the Cybermen been in hibernation when the second Doctor visited their tombs on Telos?

General/2

1. Who are the tellurians?

2. What is Galaxia Kyklos?

3. 305 were originally registered; 304 were deactivated. What were they?

4. Name the god of (a) the Sevateem; (b) the people of Sarn; (c) the Tigellans; (d) the Atlanteans encountered by the second Doctor; (e) the Tribe of Gum.

5. The Minyans called them time-ships of the gods. What

were they?
6. Which incarnation of the Doctor has never met any of his other selves?
7. Which of the following foes has the Doctor met only once? The Celestial Toymaker, Icthar, the Dalek Emperor, the Borad.
8. Name all the occasions when the Doctor has visited Italy.
9. Who did Chessene pick to be her consort?
10. Name the witch who (a) guided the Graf Vynda Ka through the catacombs of Ribos; (b) attempted to prevent the opening of the barrow at Devil's End; (c) was put into a state of shock after encountering a creature that feeds on death itself.
11. The Doctor has twice witnessed the destruction of planet Earth in two totally different situations. Name these two situations.
12. The rising and falling of the TARDIS's time rotor indicates that the machine is in flight. What function is being performed when the instrumentation within the control column revolves?
13. Shortly after his second and third regenerations the Doctor headed straight for his TARDIS. Where did he keep the key?
14. Identify the following members of the theatrical profession encountered by the Doctor: (a) The Doctor gave him a keepsake of a control circuit from a Terileptil machine; (b) The Doctor claimed that he had helped him to write one of his greatest plays; (c) He owned a restaurant in Seville and was an avid collector of butterflies; (d) The Doctor was responsible for his death when he helped in his investigations of psychic power; (e) He was the servant of a warmonger from the future.
15. Which planets visited by the Doctor have (a) three suns; (b) two suns; (c) six 'suns'?

The Adventures of the Third Doctor/3

1. The people of Inter Minor were a particularly xeno-phobic race. Why?

2. Name the Chinese assistant of Emil Keller who assisted him in the installation of the Keller Machine at Stangmoor Prison.
3. Which military regime encountered by the third Doctor proclaimed that 'Unity Is Strength'?
4. Arriving on Peladon, the Doctor and Jo were mistaken for the chairman delegate from Earth and a royal observer. How did the two travellers explain away their lack of any positive proof of identification?
5. How did the Doctor first hope to track down the source of the power which was bringing prehistoric monsters to twentieth-century London?
6. What deceit did the Marshal of Skybase plan to ensure that the Solonian Independence Conference would fail?
7. Attacked by Kronos in the TARDIS, the Doctor was cast out into the time vortex. How did Jo rescue him?
8. The Silurians possessed a third eye in their foreheads. What uses could this eye be put to?
9. Why did General Carrington hate the Martian Ambassadors so much?
10. Who was Greg Sutton?
11. What was the ultimate destination of the nerve gas warhead of the Thunderbolt missile whose transportation was being supervised by UNIT?
12. Upon learning that Vorg's Scope contained miniaturised life forms, the Inter Minorans immediately ordered its destruction. Why?
13. What was the royal emblem of Peladon?
14. Name the Galactic Federation delegate who became the Federation's Ambassador to Peladon.
15. Who ruled Solos?
16. Into whose care was the Lady Jojogrant put when the TARDIS brought her to ancient Atlantis?
17. Who travelled to the Moon to secure the Doctor's release from the penal colony there?
18. The Martians, Izlyr and Ssorg, were on Peladon on a peaceful mission. The Doctor, however, initially suspected them of having which more nefarious intentions?
19. What is Beltane?
20. Which great Chinese leader did the third Doctor claim to have accompanied on his long march?

1. Why was Duggan in Paris at the time of the Doctor and Romana's holiday in that city?
2. What was the purpose of the refinery on Delta Three?
3. How did Vorus hope to help his planet attain its former greatness?
4. Who set a trap for the Doctor at the Pavilion of Summer Winds?
5. Name the enormous mobile green brain encountered by the Doctor and Romana.
6. Why did Zastor request the Doctor's aid on Tigella?
7. Name two members of the underground peace party on Atrios at the time of the Doctor and Romana's visit to that planet.
8. Karn was once the home world of a great civilisation. What happened to it?
9. Who was Ivo?
10. What natural phenomena accompany the death of a Keeper of Traken?
11. Who sent a distress call from the Titan Base which was picked up by the Doctor and Leela?
12. Who was Bisham?
13. The Ogri's home world was Ogros, an unpleasant world of swamps containing amino acids. The Ogri depended on the protein found in these swamps for their survival. What substitute did they use on Earth?
14. On the planet which had formed around the P7E, what lay at the centre of the 'Tree of Life', protected by invisible 'dragons'?
15. What exactly was the Company on Pluto?
16. Who proclaimed himself to a Sontaran to be a member of the true warrior class of Earth? Why?
17. On which planet did the Doctor assist in the coronation of a King 'George'?
18. The Doctor attempted to halt Solon's evil schemes by overpowering him with cyanide, which he introduced into the ventilation system of the scientist's base. Why was the Morbius monster unaffected by this gas?
19. Who was Tala?
20. On Traken the Doctor and Adric detected mysterious

energy emissions similar to those produced by the Doctor's TARDIS. What was the cause of, these emissions?

The Daleks and the Thals/3

1. Why did the Daleks construct duplicates of the Doctor, Tegan and Turlough?
2. Rightly suspicious of his Dalek 'allies', the treacherous Mavic Chen prepared a secret army ready to defeat the Daleks on Kembel and to seize the Time Destructor for himself. Where was this army stationed?
3. The Kaled Scientific Elite originally intended to develop weapons to end the bitter war of attrition between themselves and the Thals. When this proved futile, what line of research did they then pursue?
4. The Doctor, Ian and Barbara and Susan believed that they had totally destroyed the Daleks on Skaro. How then did the first Doctor explain their presence on twentieth-century Earth?
5. Who destroyed the catacombs on Necros and Davros's Daleks?
6. Name the member of Commander Lytton's special guard who led the Doctor into a trap.
7. Why did Davros bear a particular hatred for Earth and indeed expressed a wish to destroy it?
8. Name all the times that the Doctor has visited Skaro.
9. Informed of the opposition to his plans by Gharman and other members of the Kaled Scientific Elite, how did Davros plot to quell this opposition?
10. How did Styles plan to destroy Davros and the Daleks on board the prison space station?
11. Who was Colonel Archer?
12. Name the Kaled scientist who arranged the annihilation of his own people to further his own evil ends.
13. How were the Daleks defeated on Mars?
14. Which of the Doctor's companions partially succumbed to distronic toxaemia on Skaro?
15. Who was Galloway in (a) *Resurrection of the Daleks*? (b) *Death to the Daleks*?

1. What was the Myrka?
2. Why was Andrew Verney imprisoned in Little Hodcombe?
3. Who was Timanov?
4. What was the ultimate aim of the Gravis and his Tractators on Frontios?
5. What is a Total Survival Suit?
6. In the twenty-first century the Earth was divided into two hostile power blocs. Name the two agents of the opposing power who had infiltrated Sea Base Four.
7. Why did Sharaz Jek bear such a great hatred towards Morgus?
8. Why did Tegan and Nyssa initially believe Mawdryn to be the Doctor?
9. Name the leader of the Earth colonists on Frontios shortly before the Doctor's arrival on that planet. Who succeeded him?
10. How was Captain Briggs's space freighter able to travel 64 million years back in time?
11. What was the fallacy of the Flesh Time which led the Doctor to suspect that Monarch was, in fact, flesh and blood?
12. The source of the Portreeve's great wisdom was his tapestry. What lay behind it?
13. Upon first meeting the TARDIS crew Lieutenant Scott presumed that they were responsible for the murder of seven of Professor Kyle's fellow archaeologists. How was he persuaded of the time-travellers' innocence?
14. The Tereleptils encountered by the Doctor had escaped from the tinclavic mines on Raaga. For the almost exclusive use of which people did the Tereleptils mine this ore?
15. Who was Stotz?
16. What are mud bursts? Which planet visited by the Doctor and Peri was plagued by them?
17. What is Numismation Gas?
18. Name the Commander and two other members of Sea Base Four at the time of the attack by the Silurians and Sea Devils.

19. Who danced the Dance of the Snake?
20. Why did Trau Morgus kill his President on Androzani Major?

Companions of the Doctor/3

1. Which of the Doctor's companions was chosen to be the Queen of the May? What was to have been her ultimate fate?
2. The use by many of his companions of Americanisms has often driven the Doctor to despair; it therefore seems mildly ironic that his latest travelling companion is an American. But which of the Doctor's companions was described by the Time Lord as 'fast becoming prey to every cliché-ridden convention in the American West'?
3. Name the home planet of the following companions of the Doctor: (a) Susan; (b) Turlough; (c) Vicki; (d) Nyssa; (e) Adric; (f) Romana.
4. Name the Doctor's two robotic companions.
5. Which of his companions did the Doctor take on a tour of his brain?
6. Name Jamie's father.
7. How did Sarah Jane prove to Mark that the spaceship on which they were supposedly travelling to a New Earth was, in fact, a fake?
8. Which of the Doctor's companions was taken over by the Three Who Rule?
9. Turlough was an orphan whose affairs were handled by a solicitor in London. Who in reality was this solicitor?
10. How did Tlotoxl and Tonila attempt to prove that Barbara was not a god?
11. Several of Tegan's relatives have been caught up in the Doctor's adventures. Name (a) her aunt who was murdered by the Master; (b) her favourite cousin who was captured by Omega; (c) her grandfather.
12. For how long was Turlough exiled to Earth? Who promised to end his exile? Why was he finally allowed to return home?
13. In which adventure did Jamie 'lose' his face? Why?

14. Who took over Adric's room on board the TARDIS?
15. All the Doctor's regenerations, save one, have been observed by his friends. Indeed in one instance it is most unlikely that the Time Lord would have survived without help from his companions. Name all those who have witnessed the regeneration of the Time Lord.

The Adventures of the Sixth Doctor/3

1. Why did the Doctor and Peri visit Varos?
2. Give the karm names of Shockeye and Chessene.
3. Where was the Rani's base situated when the Doctor and Peri encountered her in nineteenth-century England?
4. Name the girlfriend of Oscar Botcherby who also worked at *Las Cadenas* restaurant in Seville.
5. What brought the Doctor and Peri to Necros?
6. What was the temporal and spatial destination of the Kontron Tunnel created by the Timelash?
7. Name the two Maylins at the time of the Doctor's second visit to Karfel.
8. What was the main source of income on Varos?
9. Arriving on the devastated Space Station J7 and discovering that his second incarnation was not, as he supposed, dead, how did the sixth Doctor discover the location of his former self?
10. Name the Chief Embalmer of Necros. How was he killed?
11. Who was President Vargos?
12. Which of the Doctor's enemies proclaimed the flesh of a rat to be rank, but suspected it might be palatable if smoke-dried?
13. The fifth Doctor defeated the Mara on Deva Loka by surrounding it in a circle of mirrors. Unable to face its own evil, the creature was banished to the dark places of the inside. But why had the Borad banned all mirrors on Karfel?
14. Who did Sil suspect the Doctor and Peri to be?
15. Who was Tasambeker?
16. Which race of aliens encountered by the sixth Doctor

are unable to live in temperatures above freezing point?

17. Every TARDIS is equipped with a chameleon circuit enabling it to change its appearance to blend in with its surroundings. The Doctor's is, of course, inoperative, although in his fourth incarnation he did travel to Logopolis to have it repaired. When did the sixth Doctor attempt to repair this circuit, and how successful was he?

18. Name Stike's henchman on twentieth-century Earth.

19. Who was the actor who so upset the British Council that he was forced to take over the management of a restaurant in Spain?

20. What is vaskil?

The Adventures of the First Doctor/4

1. Trapped in the Celestial Toymaker's domain, Dodo and Steven were instructed to 'hunt the key that fits the door, that leads out on the Dancing Floor'. What was the Dancing Floor and where exactly was the key hidden?

2. Who was Warrien?

3. Name the 'landlord' and 'landlady' of the inn where Napoleon and Paul Barras met.

4. How did the Monoids communicate at the time of each of the Doctor's two visits to the Space Ark?

5. Arriving in the twentieth century after their adventures in revolution-torn France, the time-travellers discovered a world populated with dead earthworms, ants and flies. Why were these creatures dead?

6. Why were the Zarbi unable to enter the TARDIS when the time-machine landed on Vortis?

7. What ailment did the first Doctor share with the mighty Kublai Khan?

8. Trapped on the Sense Sphere, the TARDIS crew were obviously unable to escape in their ship as it was in Captain Maitland's possession. Why would they have been unable to escape in the TARDIS even if they could have reached it?

9. Who were Clara and Joey?

10. Who trapped Blossom Lefavre in a saw mill?

11. Which race of people had charted the Doctor's journeying through time and space?
12. The Space Ark, though huge, had only a limited carrying capacity. How then was it possible for so many Humans to travel on board the ship?
13. Where on Dido did the confrontation between the Doctor and Koquillion take place?
14. The Menoptera's cell destructor was effective only when fired at what part of the Animus?
15. Why did the Animus show such great interest in the TARDIS's Astral Map?
16. After leaving Mexico, the TARDIS materialised but continued to move. Why?
17. Name the home planet of the Drahvins.
18. Who was Ben Daheer?
19. For which classical music did Vicki once show to have a great love?
20. What is Zaphra Gas?

The Adventures of the Second Doctor/4

1. Why did Madeleine Issigri originally join forces with Maurice Caven?
2. To halt the advance of the Great Intelligence's web, it was decided to blow up Charing Cross Station. Unknown to the army the Doctor was at the station when the orders to detonate were given. How did he survive the blast?
3. How did the second Doctor attempt to persuade Group Marshall Stike to release him from the Spanish dungeon in which he was imprisoned?
4. Salamander was known as the Shopkeeper of the World. How did he hope to alleviate famine in the world?
5. Why did the Master Brain in the Land of Fiction want to take over Earth?
6. What is a ghanta?
7. The Island of Death on Dulkis was soaked in radiation when the Dulcians exploded an atomic bomb there. 172 years later the Doctor, Zoe and Jamie arrived there

and found the island to be radiation-free. What was the reason for this?

8. Milo Clancey and Dom Issigri were close friends and formed a mining partnership. Why did Madeleine Issigri dissolve this partnership?

9. What function did the Androgums serve on Dastari's space station?

10. How did the Doctor save Vana from the Krotons' dispersion unit?

11. Which race of aliens encountered by the second Doctor are blind?

12. How did the Doctor finally defeat the Dominators on Dulkis?

13. Who contemptuously referred to the second Doctor as a 'clown' when he was in the company of a 'dandy'?

14. Apart from his obvious hostility towards the time-travellers, why did the Doctor have severe misgivings about Tobias Vaughn?

15. Exactly what kept alive the inhabitants of the Land of Fiction?

16. What is the 'Earth for Earth' group?

17. Name all the survivors of the Sontarans' massacre of Space Station J7.

18. What manner of craft were General Hermack's Minnows?

19. How did the Doctor defeat Medusa in the Land of Fiction?

20. Who was Perkins in *The Highlanders*?

Who Said What?

All the following quotes have been taken from Target novelisations of *Doctor Who* stories. Identify them.

1. 'If you could touch the alien sand with your feet, hear the cries of strange birds, watch them wheel above you in another sky... would that satisfy you?'

2. 'BOW DOWN BEFORE ME, PLANETS. BOW DOWN, O STARS. BOW DOWN, O GALAXIES, AND WORSHIP... THE *ME*, THE GREAT ALL-

3. 'He killed my step-mother, and then my father ... and now this! The world I grew up in – blotted out forever!'

4. 'Homo sapiens ... what an indomitable species ... it is only a few million years since it crawled up out of the sea and learned to walk ... a puny, defenceless biped ... it has survived flood, plague, famine, war ... and now here it is out among the stars ... awaiting a new life. That's something for you to be proud of.'

5. 'We are entombed here, but we still live on. This is only the beginning. We will prepare. We will grow stronger. When the time is right, we will emerge. We shall build our own City. We ... will be the supreme power in the Universe ... !'

6. 'Harry Sullivan is an imbecile!'

7. 'Our lives are different from everybody else's, that's the exciting thing. Nobody in the universe, in the whole universe, can do what we're doing, be what we are. Nobody.'

8. 'You made us, Man of Evil. But we are free.'

9. 'When all other life-forms are supressed, when the Daleks are the supreme power of the Universe, then we shall have peace. All wars will end. The Daleks are the power not of evil but of good!'

10. 'I was born in another time, another world.'

11. 'A hero? I should have been a god!'

12. '*We* shall not destroy the humans, Doctor. The ape-primitives will do it themselves. We shall merely provide them with the pretext for doing so ... And these *humans* will die as they have lived – in a sea of their own blood.'

13. 'Suppose somebody who knew the future told you that a certain child would grow up to be an evil dictator – could you then destroy that child? ... I could destroy the Daleks here and now. But do I have the right?'

14. 'Three of 'em! I didn't know when I was well off!'

15. 'Call yourself a Time Lord! A broken clock keeps better time than you. At least it's right twice a day, which is more than you are!'

16. 'Waking, sleeping, you can never escape me, Turlough!'

17. 'I shall be President Eternal and rule forever!'

18. 'I put *myself* among the gods! And now I shall liberate

my people. With me as their leader we shall reign over
all other beings.'

19. 'I know you think I'm insane, that I want power for its
own sake. But you're wrong. The world is weak, a chaos
of conflicting ideals. It needs a strong, single-minded
leader. I was to be that leader...'

20. 'Feeling? Yes, we know of this weakness of yours. We
are fortunate. We do not possess feelings.'

The Adventures of the Third Doctor/4

1. What was the Plain of Stones on Spiridon?
2. What rule is enshrined in paragraph fifty-nine, sub-
section two of the Galactic Federation's Articles of
Peace? Why was this particular rule so pertinent to the
Doctor during his first trip to Peladon?
3. Name the first person to be transformed into a mutant
at Project Inferno.
4. Who are the Chronivores? What is their domain?
5. Who was Fu Peng?
6. Why could no Human travel unprotected on the surface
of Solos during the hours of daylight?
7. Who was Miss Paget?
8. How was the Draconian Emperor finally convinced of
the truth of the Doctor's claim that the Draconian
spacecraft were not being attacked by Earthmen?
9. Name the astronaut on the Mars Probe Six flight who
became the head of the Space Security Department.
10. The crystal used by the Master in his TOMTIT experiments was, in fact, only part of the infinitely more
powerful Great Crystal of Kronos. Where was this to be
found?
11. Which element has rightly been described as the
'chameleon of elements'?
12. Why was Barnham able to neutralise the evil forces of
the Keller Machine?
13. What technological marvel was to be found at the
Newton Institute at Wootton near Cambridge?
14. After the Doctor's sentence to a duel to the death in the
Pit of Combat with Grun, King Peladon's Champion,

the remaining members of the Galactic Federation's Board of Assessment took a vote on whether to leave the planet or not. Who voted to remain and help the Doctor? Why?

15. Why was Professor Sondergaard forced to take refuge in the thaesium mines of Peladon?

16. What 'pet' did the Silurians keep in the caves underneath Wenley Moor?

17. Finally convinced of the imminent destruction of his world, how did Brigade Leader Lethbridge-Stewart propose to escape the coming disaster?

18. Who killed the Brigade Leader?

19. Who stole important state documents from the suite of General Cheng Teik, the Chinese delegate to an international peace conference? Why?

20. TOMTIT was an acronym for Transmission Of Matter Through Interstitial Time. What is interstitial time?

Adventures in History/4

1. How did Barbara foolishly attempt to rewrite history in sixteenth-century Mexico?

2. Who were the Myth Makers?

3. Name the old friend of Marcus Scarman who came to investigate his disappearance and was later killed on the orders of Marcus.

4. What parting gifts did the TARDIS crew receive from Lady Cranleigh?

5. What was the invention of George Stephenson which the Doctor promised would take off like a rocket?

6. How did the time-travellers finally re-enter the tomb of Yetaxa where the TARDIS had landed?

7. After the defeat of the corrupt solicitor Grey, Lieutenant Algernon Thomas Alfred Ffinch of Colonel Atwood's Rifles gave the Doctor, Polly, Ben and Jamie safe escort across the Scottish glens. Why?

8. Why did the Clantons send Seth Harper into Tombstone?

9. How was the Doctor indirectly responsible for the death of Hector the Trojan?

10. What ruse did the Doctor and Ian use to escape from the Earl of Leicester and his men in Palestine?
11. Where was Kublai Khan's summer palace to be found?
12. How did Diomede the Greek enter the gates of Troy?
13. Who pretended to be a Senior Citizen from the Southern Provinces of France who needed a uniform befitting his rank? How did he obtain these required clothes?
14. The Doctor and Sarah Jane attempted to foil Sutekh's plan to break free of his tomb by exploding the rocket, which was to destroy the Pyramids of Mars, with gelignite. Why did their plan fail?
15. Who betrayed Barbara's presence in El Akir's harem?
16. How did the crew of Captain Briggs's space freighter return to their own century after being transported 65 million years back in time?
17. The Doctor once claimed that he caught a prize salmon in the River Fleet, a tributuary of the Thames which once followed a course equivalent to the area covered by Fleet Street today. With whom did he share this salmon?
18. Who rescued Vicki from the destruction of Troy?
19. Landing on the plateau of the Pamir in 1289 Susan discovered in the snows the footprint of a giant. What was it in reality?
20. Place the following adventures in their chronological order in the history of Earth: *Timelash*; *Pyramids of Mars*; *The Time Meddler*; *The Awakening*; *Time-Flight*; *The Visitation*.

The Adventures of the Fourth Doctor/4

1. What was the principal weapon of the Taran nobility?
2. How did Professor Kerensky hope to alleviate the world's food shortage?
3. Who were the Ajacks?
4. The people of the Starliner had spent many generations preparing the Starliner for take-off. Why was it impossible for them to do so until the Doctor's intervention?

5. Who was the Caber?
6. What was the Key to the Race Banks of the Minyan people?
7. With what was Vivien Fay's wand powered?
8. How did Mena hope to make use of Hardin's experiments in tachyonics to boost the flagging economy of the Leisure Hive?
9. What is a tachyon?
10. Who set the TARDIS's co-ordinates on the toss of a coin?
11. The Galsec team were a military expedition searching for a missing freighter when they were lured down to an 'uninhabited' Earth. Nine men came down, but the Doctor, Harry and Sarah Jane met only five. What had become of the others?
12. Why did Meglos instruct the Gaztaks to kidnap an Earthling?
13. Name the Swampie spy in the refinery on Delta Three.
14. What use was Solon's base on Karn originally put to?
15. Who was a direct descendant of the High Kings of Tara, and Mistress of the Domains of Thervalde, Moretegarde and Freya?
16. Which two crewmembers on board the Sandminer were descendants of the Founding Families?
17. What manner of space transportation do the Moothi use?
18. Who was de Vries?
19. Which 'friend' of the Doctor brought Nyssa to Logopolis?
20. What was the 'Time Lord spell' to be found on the two gifts the Doctor left Ohica on Karn?

The Adventures of the Fifth Doctor/4

1. How long had the Tractators been on Frontios before the arrival of the Doctor?
2. Who was Dugdale?
3. What is the Misos Triangle?
4. At the time of the Doctor and Peri's visit to the planet, who controlled the supplies of spectrox on Androzani

Minor?

5. What unusual 'weapon' did Turlough use against the colonists on Frontios

6. How did the Terileptil Leader on Earth correctly deduce that the TARDIS crew were aliens?

7. With what manner of missiles was Sea Base Four armed?

8. Which of the Elders of Sarn had met his god near the summit of the Fire Mountain? What was this 'god' in reality?

9. Why was Sharaz Jek so interested in the Doctor and Peri?

10. What images did Kalid conjure up in his attempt to dissuade Tegan and Nyssa from entering the Sanctum in which was to be found the Xeraphin life force?

11. The community in the Dome on Deva Loka took military efficiency to an almost absurd degree. What do the following acronyms stand for? (a) TSS; (b) ILF; (c) ZMI; (d) TAD.

12. How did the Doctor destroy the projection of the Malus which had infiltrated the TARDIS?

13. Who was Colonel Periera?

14. Name three of the inhabitants of Castrovalva encountered by the TARDIS crew.

15. Name Icthar's two Silurian colleagues who assisted him in the take-over of Sea Base Four.

16. In which year did the Doctor, Tegan and Turlough arrive in the midst of battles between Cavaliers and Roundheads?

17. Name the doctor at Brendon Public School.

18. Who was Norna?

19. Name the commander of the Sea Devil warriors encountered by the fifth Doctor.

20. How did Captain Revere die?

The Cybermen/3

1. How did the Cybermen attempt to alter the course of Earth history?

2. Who regarded himself as the Resurrector of the

Cybermen?

3. Why is gold so lethal to Cybermen?
4. Why did Professor Kyle call in the help of Lieutenant Scott and his troopers in 2526? Name one other member of Lieutenant Scott's team.
5. Who recognised the Doctor and Jamie from Planet 14?
6. Name the two instances in which the Doctor has met the Cyber Controller.
7. General Cutler, the head of the Snowcap Ice Base, proposed using the deadly Z-Bomb to destroy Mondas. What was the Doctor's plan?
8. Name Captain Briggs's first officer.
9. The entrance doors to the Cybermen's Tombs, when closed, completed a circuit which released a fatal electric current. Who closed these doors and, in so doing, sacrificed his own life?
10. On the Earth of 2526 the Doctor succeeded in preventing the Cybermen from exploding their bomb – a bomb which would have destroyed the planet. Exactly how did he do this?
11. Who vowed that the Cybermen would never leave Telos? Why?
12. Who fell into the Cybermen's deadly trap on Telos? What was this trap?
13. In the event of their bomb being defused on twenty-sixth-century Earth, the Cybermen had developed a contingency plan. What was it?
14. How was Cyber Control destroyed in *Attack of the Cybermen*?
15. How did the Cybermen plan to destroy the Earth in *Attack of the Cybermen*?

The Adventures of the Sixth Doctor/4

1. What was the Mark of the Rani?
2. On which planet was the Garden of Fond Memories to be found?
3. Who plotted to become Governor of Governors and Viceroy of Varos?
4. What particular attraction did the Great Lakes of

Pandatorea hold for the sixth Doctor?
5. Who was Kara?
6. Who was Vogel?
7. Name the Master of Jaconda before the coming of Mestor.
8. When the Doctor and Peri travelled to Karfel it was the second time the Doctor had visited that planet. When was his previous visit?
9. Who was Lord Ravensworth?
10. What is the Weed Plant?
11. Before leaving Space Station J7 Chessene took the precaution of bringing with her to Earth several cannisters of coronic acid. Why?
12. Stranded on twentieth-century Earth Lytton sent out an intergalactic distress call which was picked up by the Cryons who then enlisted the mercenary's aid. Why did the Cryons need Lytton's help?
13. Who was the Doña Arana?
14. How was the Governor of Varos elected at the time of the Doctor and Peri's visit to that planet?
15. What was the usual fate of rebels on Karfel?
16. Why was the Doctor so necessary to the plans of Chessene and the Sontarans?
17. Why did Orcini free the Doctor, Natasha and Grigory from their prison on Necros?
18. Who were Etta and Arak on Varos?
19. Who attempted to exorcise the Doctor and then travelled with him in the TARDIS – taking notes as he did so?
20. What was Chessene's ultimate ambition?

The Adventures of the First Doctor/5

1. How did the Drahvins hope to persuade the Doctor and Vicki to destroy the Rills?
2. Who was Wigner?
3. For whom did the Animus first mistake the TARDIS crew?
4. Bennett disguised himself as Koquillion to intimidate Vicki and to lend support to his claim that the

Didonians were a savage and murderous people. What was the real use of the costume he wore?

5. How were the TARDIS crew warned of the great danger facing them on Xeros?

6. Name the two members of Jano's race who took Steven and Dodo on a tour of their city.

7. Twelve Rills were attacked by the Drahvins in space. How many survived to crashland on the doomed planet?

8. After having taken Ian and Barbara from the security of the twentieth century, why was the Doctor unable to return them home?

9. Exactly how did the Animus spread itself over the surface of Vortis?

10. Who was Ashton in *The Dalek Invasion of Earth*? What was his ultimate fate?

11. Name the security officer at the GPO Tower at the time of the invasion of London by the War Machines.

12. A man of peace, the Doctor has often been forced to use violence, and has killed – with great reluctance – many creatures for the greater good. But which man did the first Doctor cold-heartedly attempt to murder so he would not impede the TARDIS crew's progress back to the time-machine?

13. How did the Optera propose to kill Ian and Vrestin before the Earthman and the Menoptera gained their trust?

14. Anxiously awaiting the arrival of a ship to rescue her and Bennett from Dido, Vicki detected a signal on her radar. The rescue ship, however, had over 69 flying hours to cover before reaching the planet. What had Vicki spotted on the radar?

15. Where was it forbidden to dump bodies in the river?

15. The Zarbi established a slave colony at the Crater of Needles. How did they ensure that their Menoptera prisoners could not fly away?

17. Who brought the TARDIS, with a frightened Vicki inside, into Troy?

18. The Rills and Drahvins believed that the planet on which they were stranded had fourteen days to doomsday. How did the Doctor discover that it had, in fact, only two days before destruction?

19. Who was Mellium?
20. Bored with Time Lord life, the Doctor and Susan left their home planet of Gallifrey in the constellation of Kasterborous. But do we have any indication of *when* they left?

The Adventures of the Fourth Doctor/5

1. How did Scaroth die?
2. Who embarked on the Great Journey of Life and, in so doing, devastated countless planets?
3. Name four members of the Sevateem.
4. Why did Prince Reynart plan to send an android double of himself to his coronation?
5. How did Marcus Scarman die?
6. Why was Cordo about to kill himself on Pluto when the Doctor and Leela arrived on that planet?
7. Many natives of Chloris fell victim to the Creature from the Pit. Erato, however, was a peaceful ambassador to the planet. Why did he kill so many Chlorissans?
8. How did Meglos attempt to stop the Doctor and Romana from visiting Tigella? How did they foil his plan?
9. Which young Alzarian witnessed the dying moments of Decider Draith?
10. The Skonnan battle cruiser was carrying a cargo of seven hymetusite crystals. It arrived with only five. Why?
11. The Think Tank was a highly secret research complex, and security precautions were extremely tight. How then did Sarah Jane and Harry gain admittance?
12. Who was on the same technical course as the Doctor some 450 years ago, and when meeting the Doctor again greeted him by his Time Lord identification of Theta Sigma?
13. What pathetic excuse did Tryst give the Doctor for smuggling vraxoin?
14. Taken over by the Wirrn, Noah spoke of the 'great blackness'. What was it?
15. Who were Torvin, Edu and Ainu?

16. In his evil schemes, Borusa attempted to lift the Doctor and Romana from their time streams and send them to the Death Zone on Gallifrey. Where exactly on Earth did he pick them up?
17. Forgill Castle was on the banks of which large lake?
18. Who was the Heresiarch of Argolis? Who was his consort?
19. Where did Mandrel and his fellow rebels hide from the Company on Pluto?
20. How did Zargo, Camilla and Aukon die?

The Adventures of the Fifth Doctor/5

1. Sharaz Jek seemed always to be one step ahead of General Chellak. Why?
2. Although the first Doctor seemed to have little knowledge of cricket, and indeed betrayed his ignorance of the game when the TARDIS took himself, Steven and Sara Kingdom to a match at the Oval in London, the fifth Doctor was a devoted follower of that most gentlemanly of sports. But how did the Doctor's prowess with the cricket ball actually help to save his life in space?
3. What was so odd about the *Chronicle of Castrovalva* which was to be found in Shardovan's library?
4. Who were Amyand and Roskal?
5. Why was the Doctor so reluctant to visit Frontios when the TARDIS materialised in orbit around the planet? Why was he finally obliged to land there?
6. Who was Hippo?
7. Where exactly in Little Hodcombe did the TARDIS first materialise?
8. How did the Doctor destroy the Silurians and the Sea Devils who had taken over Sea Base Four?
9. For Mawdryn and his fellow scientists to find death for which they so longed, the Doctor reluctantly agreed to sacrifice his eight remaining regenerations. What energy source finally proved to be the means to grant the scientists eternal peace?
10. How did the Doctor succeed in escaping the androids

which were holding Peri, Salateen and himself prisoner in Sharaz Jek's lair on Androzani Minor?

11. Why were the bodies of the colonists so useful to the Tractators on Frontios?

12. Name the paradise world visited by the fifth Doctor which was free of predatory animals and diseases and had a comfortable temperature constant within a five degree range.

13. On what did Enlightenment and Persuasion base the human forms which they assumed on their way to Earth? Why did they think it necessary to adopt these forms?

14. In which adventure did the fifth Doctor repair and refurbish the TARDIS console?

15. Who was Ben Wolsey?

16. How did the Terileptils control their human slaves?

17. The Mara is unable to face its own evil and the Doctor defeated it on Deva Lok by encircling it with mirrors. What did the Time Lord use as mirrors?

18. Why did Princess Villagra remain silent the entire time she was on board Monarch's ship?

19. What is artron energy?

20. How did Sharaz Jek die?

Companions of the Doctor/4

1. Kamelion was discovered by the Master when the evil Time Lord was stranded on Xeriphas. How was he destroyed?

2. Why was Victoria not present with her friends when the Doctor and Jamie did battle with Chessene and her allies?

3. Which of the Doctor's companions was determined that Eldrad must live?

4. In which adventure did Dodo and Steven meet a King and Queen?

5. Which of the Doctor's companions was almost murdered by a ventriloquist's dummy?

6. Tegan first met the Brigadier on the date of which national celebration?

7. Who tried to teach Leela the fine art of tea drinking, with very little success?

8. Which of the Doctor's companions succeeded in giving a computer a nervous breakdown, destroyed a fleet of Cyberships – but did not know what candles were?

9. Who was amorously pursued by a mad Roman Emperor?

10. What traditional means did the Doctor sometimes use to contact K9?

11. Where did Tegan meet herself?

12. Which of his companions did the Doctor, in his capacity of President of the Time Lords, banish from the Capitol on Gallifrey? Why?

13. Name Turlough's brother. What became of the rest of his family?

14. Which member of the TARDIS crew was acclaimed by the Doctor to be a 'wizard of the ivory keys'?

15. Which of the Doctor's companions was (a) a member of the Imperial Clans on his home planet? (b) an aristocrat whose home planet was destroyed by the machinations of the Master? (c) a lady of the Doctor's own race whose academic achievements were somewhat superior to his?

The Adventures of the Sixth Doctor/5

1. How did Mestor plan to spread the seed of his species throughout the Universe?

2. Give the reasons for Chessene and the Sontarans choosing to continue their time-travel experiments on Earth.

3. Anxious to gain power on Varos, Sil called in an invasion force from his home planet. Why did it never reach Varos?

4. What last favour did Orcini ask of the Doctor?

5. Who saved Peri from being turned into a tree?

6. Name two of Lytton's colleagues in his proposed diamond robbery.

7. How did the Doctor save Karfel from the deadly missile aimed at that planet by the Bandrils?

8. How was Shockeye able to track down so unerringly the wounded sixth Doctor in Spain?
9. Who was Maldak?
10. The Master is an expert hypnotist but the Rani controls people's minds by what other method?
11. Name the squire of Orcini.
12. What great gift did Chessene promise to the Sontarans?
13. Why was the amulet worn by the Maylin of Karfel so important to the Borad?
14. How did Kara die?
15. After the defeat of Davros, what other means of revenue did the Doctor suggest to Takis?
16. What peculiar properties do Kontron Crystals possess?
17. How did the Doctor kill Shockeye?
18. How was Azmael instrumental in the destruction of Mestor?
19. Why were Lord Ravensworth's men so extraordinarily violent at the time of the Doctor's visit to nineteenth-century England?
20. Name two of the Karfelon rebels at the time of the Doctor's second visit to Karfel.

General/3

1. The Pirate Captain was particularly interested in Earth because of its abundant quantities of quartz. On which planets are the following minerals to be found in abundance? (a) thaesium; (b) zeiton 7; (c) trisilicate; (d) gold; (e) vaskil.
2. What is a Kontron Tunnel?
3. Name the one instance when the Doctor has purpose-fully travelled through time and space to meet one of his other selves.
4. Which three apparently contradictory explanations has *Doctor Who* provided for the destruction of Atlantis?
5. Who was (a) Professor Hayter? (b) Professor Howard Foster? (c) Professor Chronotis?
6. Name all the circumstances in which the Doctor has been minituarised.
7. In which adventure was the Doctor mistaken for (a) a

Federation delegate to a backward planet? (b) a dentist? (c) an unscrupulous South American dictator? (d) the Evil One?

8. Name the Doctor's two trips to Egypt.
9. Name the units of currency on the following planets: (a) Pluto; (b) Ribos.
10. Who were the Masters of Earth in 2164?
11. In 1986 a rogue planet approached the Earth. What was its name?
12. Why did it appear so familiar to observers?
13. Several of the Doctor's foes have been mindless creatures who have been manipulated by superior beings in their quest for power. Who controlled (a) the Zarbi and their Larva Guns? (b) the Tractators? (c) the Yeti?
14. In which adventure was the TARDIS seen to contain a conservatory, a medical wing and miles of brick-lined stairways and corridors?
15. With the exception of *Planet of Giants* what was the first *Doctor Who* adventure to be set totally on present day Earth?

The Daleks and the Thals/4

1. How did the Supreme Dalek intend to initiate the collapse of twentieth-century Earth society in *Resurrection of the Daleks*?
2. Disturbed by Davros's experiments in genetic mutation and his attempts to create a new race of Daleks on Necros, who called in the Daleks from Skaro to capture their creator?
3. Why did the Daleks from Skaro not exterminate the Doctor when they met him on Necros?
4. What plans did the Daleks have for the Humans after their mining operations on twenty-second-century Earth were completed?
5. Who destroyed the space station which had held Davros prisoner, and, in so doing, destroyed the Daleks on the space station and in their own spacecraft?
6. Who was Professor Laird?

7. Which top SSS agent was charged with the task of killing the 'traitors' Bret Vyon, the Doctor and Steven?
8. What means did the Daleks, encountered by the first Doctor on Skaro, use for growing food?
9. How did Marc Cory hope to warn his galaxy about the Daleks' Master Plan?
10. What was to be found on the fourth level of the ruined Kaled city on Skaro?
11. What were the entry and exit points of the Dalek Time Corridor along which the Doctor, Tegan and Turlough travelled?
12. What was the Daleks' Operation Inferno?
13. What two traps did the Daleks set for the Doctor in *Resurrection of the Daleks*?
14. Why did the Daleks need the fifth Doctor so?
15. How did Davros escape the explosion of the space station which had formerly held him prisoner?

The Adventures of the Fifth Doctor/6

1. Why could the Terileptils encountered by the Doctor never return to their home planet?
2. Stotz led the gun-runners on Androzani Minor. But who was Stotz's chief?
3. For some thirty years Frontios had been bombarded by meteorite storms. What did the colonists believe to be the cause of these storms?
4. What was the true reason for these bombardments?
5. How did Will Chandler return to the seventeenth century?
6. Arriving on Androzani Minor the Doctor and Peri were sentenced to death under the red cloth. This was a method of execution previously reserved for the military where the victims' bodies were later cremated in the red cloth in which they had been executed. How did the time-travellers escape from this punishment?
7. Who took the TARDIS to Manussa?
8. Which member of the staff of Brendon School did the Black Guardian briefly impersonate, much to Turlough's distress?

9. How did the Doctor destroy the Myrka on Sea Base Four?
10. Who greeted the winners of the race for Enlightenment?
11. What were the Six Faces of Delusion?
12. What power have the people of Harkol harnessed in much the same way as the Humans have harnessed electricty on Earth?
13. With the transmitter to Mawdryn's ship destroyed, how did the Doctor guide the transmat capsule to the ship?
14. How did Striker's Eternals condition the Humans they had captured into going up on the deck to face the blackness of outer space?
15. The Place of Fire was a sacred place, forbidden to the people of Sarn. What was it?
16. How did Nilson and Solow gain control over Maddox in *Warriors of the Deep*?
17. Who was Captain Urquhart?
18. What are the Plasmatons composed of?
19. Why was the Gravis so interested in the Doctor's TARDIS?
20. What is spectrox toxaemia?

The Adventures of the Sixth Doctor/6

1. Who was the terrible Zodin?
2. How did Stike die?
3. Where exactly on Telos did the TARDIS carrying the sixth Doctor and Cybermen arrive?
4. How and where did the Doctor banish the Borad?
5. Who destroyed Davros's remaining hand on Necros?
6. Why did the Rani periodically need to visit Earth?
7. Who was Quillam?
8. How did he die?
9. What did Davros intend to do with the corpses laying in suspended animation on Necros?
10. Who was the Doctor's cellmate on Telos?
11. What was the Purple Zone in the Punishment Dome on Varos?
12. Who was Luke Ward?
13. The Doctor has often described himself as a doctor of

many things, although one of his specialties is certainly cybernetics. The Master is, of course, an expert mathematician. In which particular branch of science is the Rani particularly adept?

14. Who were Kartz and Reimer?
15. How did the Doctor enter the Rani's TARDIS on Earth?
16. Name three of the Cryons encountered by the Doctor and Peri on Telos.
17. Who was Sil's main accomplice on Varos?
18. Which aliens lurked in the London sewers underneath Fleet Street?
19. Who was Vena's father?
20. The Great Healer on Necros was better known to the Doctor by which other name?

Behind the Scenes/2

1. Name the directors of the following classic *Doctor Who* stories: (a) *The Web Planet*; (b) *The Web of Fear*; (c) *The Daemons*; (d) *Logopolis*; (e) *The Caves of Androzani*: (f) *Revelation of the Daleks*.
2. Which of these directors has also written several *Doctor Who* scripts?
3. Name the part played in *Doctor Who* by the following actors: (a) Neil Toynay; (b) James Stoker.
4. What was the first story of *Doctor Who* to be repeated on British television?
5. Terry Nation was the writer who created the Daleks. But who wrote the following Dalek stories? (a) *Resurrection of the Daleks*; (b) *Day of the Daleks*; (c) *Evil of the Daleks*; (d) *The Daleks' Master Plan*.
6. Who was Milton Subotsky?
7. Which *Doctor Who* story broke with continuity and referred to the Doctor as Doctor Who?
8. Name the Time Lords played by the following actors: (a) Richard Hurndall; (b) Lalla Ward; (c) Kate O'Mara; (d) Philip Latham; (e) Peter Butterworth.
9. Susan is, of course, the Doctor's granddaughter, and the Doctor has always displayed great affection towards

her. But in what circumstances was the Doctor seen to have another granddaughter, by the name of Barbara, and a niece called Louise?

10. Wendy Padbury is most famous for her role of the Doctor's petite companion from the future, Zoe. It is, however, little known that she has also played the part of another TARDIS crewmember. Which role did she play, and in what circumstances?

11. What was *Doctor Who and the Pescatons*?

12. Match the following actors with the roles they have played in Doctor Who:

Ian Marter	Turlough
William Russell	Steven Taylor
Matthew Waterhouse	Ian Chesterton
Mark Strickson	Adric
Peter Purves	Harry Sullivan

13. Name the three *Doctor Who* roles taken by talented actor, Martin Jarvis.

14. Which actor, who eventually became a firm friend of the Doctor's, made his first appearance in the TV series as a Yeti?

15. What was the connection between the actors who played the parts of Professor Travers and Victoria, the second Doctor's companion?

16. Name all the *Doctor Who* stories which have been filmed on foreign locations.

17. What was *Doctor Who meets Scratchman*?

18. Kevin Stoney has twice taken the role of two master villains in *Doctor Who*. Name them.

19. Which two adventures of the fourth Doctor proved to be two of the most cost-effective ever, being filmed, as they were, back-to-back, and using virtually the same set?

20. Which actor to have played the role of the Doctor was also fondly remembered as a villain in a popular and long-running BBC series?

THE ANSWERS

1. (i) his first regeneration was occasioned by old age – indeed, he was heard to remark that his old body was becoming a bit tired; (ii) the Time Lords changed his appearance for the second time so that he would not be recognised on Earth during his exile; (iii) the Doctor regenerated a third time when all the cells of his body had been destroyed by the effects of the crystals on Metebelis Three; (iv) he regenerated again when his fourth body fell from the dish scanner of the Pharos Project on Earth; (v) he regenerated for the fifth time to save himself from the fatal effects of spectrox poisoning.
2. The Brigadier who succeeded Lethbridge-Stewart as head of UNIT.
3. As a form of lighting.
4. The Macra.
5. *The Seeds of Death* (the twenty-first century); *Earthshock* (2526); *Frontier in Space* (2540); *Frontios* and *The Ark* (10 million years in the future; the second half of *The Ark* took place 700 years after the Doctor's first visit).
6. (a) Queen Elizabeth II – in fact after the affair with the Giant Robot the Doctor even turned down an invitation to dine at the palace! He claimed to the Brigade Leader that he had met King Edward VII, and to Jo that he had attended Queen Victoria's coronation; he met King Richard in Palestine. Strictly speaking, he also did not meet King John – rather he met Kamelion who was impersonating the monarch.
7. Both TARDISes materialised in Shockeye's kitchen.
8. (a) Poppea; (b) Galleia; (c) Tanha.
9. Alzarius.
10. (a) the Usurian Company; (b) the West Lodge of the Foamasi; (c) the Graf Vynda Ka.
11. (a) *The Green Death*; (b) *The Highlanders*; (c) *The Underwater Menace*; (d) *The Highlanders*.
12. The Time Lords' constitution.
13. The second and sixth Doctors who met in Seville.
14. (a) Rondal was the Varosian who helped the Doctor and Peri and was killed while doing so; (b) Rondel was an

alternative name for the Arc of Infinity.
15. (a) Anne; (b) Victoria; (c) Isobel; (d) Nyssa; (e) Norna.

The Adventures of the First Doctor/1 – page 12

1. He alone of all the Doctors realised the meaning of the riddle written in Old High Gallifreyan and found in Rassilon's tomb: 'To lose is to win, and he who wins shall lose.' He guessed that the immortality which was Borusa's right as the wearer of the Ring of Rassilon would, in fact, condemn him to a living death throughout eternity.
2. Yartek.
3. He claimed to be travelling to sue for peace with Kublai Khan on behalf of his leader, Noghai. In truth he was planning to assassinate the great Khan.
4. He rendered the Time Lord invisible, intangible and dumb, until the penultimate move in the Trilogic Game. He left the Doctor one hand with which to play the deadly game.
5. Charlie, and Kate.
6. Vortis. After the defeat of the Animus, the Menoptera were convinced that the flower forest would bloom once more.
7. The Doctor.
8. The TARDIS crew and the Daleks when they landed in quick succession on the top of the Empire State Building.
9. History. So great was her knowledge of the subject (and for obvious reasons, as later became apparent!) that, when given a copy of a book on the French Revolution (her grandfather's favourite period of Earth history), she immediately spotted an error.
10. The alligators in the sewers, encountered by Susan and David Campbell, had escaped from public zoos after the Daleks had invaded twenty-second-century Earth.
11. When the TARDIS doors opened at the point of materialisation (the most dangerous part of a journey), the 'space pressure' outside caused the travellers' size to reduce dramatically. The Doctor never did explain the

74

exact reason for the doors' swinging open, but the TARDIS's fault locator did indicate faults on mechanisms QR18 and A14D of the time-machine.

12. Gallifrey. Susan fondly described her home planet as such in *The Sensorites*.
13. To avenge the death of his brother, Hector, who had been killed by Achilles.
14. The First Elder. The Sensorites were divided into various castes, the Elders being the ruling class.
15. A rebel encountered by the time-travellers on Xeros.
16. Two of Kirksen's fellow killers on the prison planet.
17. Tor; Chal; Nanina; Wylda.
18. The Menoptera.
19. To discuss and plot the overthrow of Robespierre and set up Napoleon as leader of France.
20. The location of Captain Avery's treasure.

Adventures in History/1 – page 13

1. Will Chandler.
2. Ike, Phineas and Billy, all of whom died at the Shoot-Out at the OK Corral; and Reuben, who had been killed by Doc Holliday and to avenge whose death the Clanton brothers had come to Tombstone.
3. That of the lyre player, Maximus Pettulian, who had come to Rome to assassinate Nero.
4. He was the result of a minor aberration in Professor Whitaker's Time Scoop.
5. The TARDIS.
6. Laurence Scarman.
7. He died by falling off the roof of his burning family home.
8. The Animus on Vortis.
9. A group of assassins, so called because of their use of the drug, hashish. They served Ala-Eddin, the Old Man of the Mountains, who lived on Mount Alumet in Persia, until they were conquered by the mighty Mongol conqueror, Hulaga. Some of their number had made their lair in the Cave of Five Hundred Eyes in Tun-Huang.

10. Ping-Cho.
11. The Rani. She was also present sometime during Earth's Dark Ages, and the American War of Independence. Like the Luddite rise, such turbulent times in Earth's history proved the perfect cover for the Rani whose experiments augmented the violent side of man's nature. The Rani has also travelled to Earth during its Cretaceous period when she obtained embryos of some Tyrannasauros Rexes.
12. Isabella and Hugh.
13. Sutekh. This was a name given to the Osiran by the ancient Egyptians.
14. The Doctor, Ian and Barbara. The Aztecs believed that Barbara was the incarnation of their former high priest, Yetaxa.
15. Angered at the Senate's rejection of his plans for building a new Rome, he decided to set fire to the city. He got the idea, of course, from the Doctor who accidentally set fire to a map of Rome!
16. Linx.
17. The mute manservant of Nero. He died when his master commanded him to drink a goblet of poisoned wine.
18. Ostensibly to demand more money for the Crusades. In reality, the Master intended the Kamelion-King to stir up more ill-will towards the true King John, in his designs to prevent the signing of Magna Carta.
19. The Meddling Monk.
20. The Eocene period.

The Adventures of the Second Doctor/1 – page 14

1. *The Mind Robber*.
2. The Seed Pods were capable of absorbing the oxygen in the planet's atmosphere, thereby making Earth much more like Mars. The Pods were sent to Earth via T-Mat.
3. So that he could be present at UNIT's annual reunion.
4. A young and unorthodox Dulcian and son of Senex, the Dulcians' Director. Arranging a visit to the Island of Death he was the only one of his party to escape death by the Quarks. He later helped the Doctor, Jamie and

Zoe to defeat the Dominators.

5. Solicitor Grey.

6. Abu and Vana.

7. The influence of the Gravitron which was to be found on the Moon.

8. Tanya Lernov.

9. The colonists on the holiday planet which had been threatened by the Macra. This was to be in honour of the TARDIS crew's defeat of the evil creatures.

10. This was a pseudonym adopted by a 'chameleonised' Polly who took her place at Chameleon Tours' reception desk in *The Faceless Ones*.

11. The Doctor was sentenced to execution by firing squad; Zoe was sentenced to twenty years' imprisonment in a civilian gaol; and Jamie was to be returned to his Highland regiment which he had supposedly deserted.

12. Lemuel Gulliver, whom the time-travellers met in the Land of Fiction.

13. He was sent there by the Time Lords to investigate the time-travel experiments of Kartz and Reimer. The Gallifreyans feared that these experiments, which were causing ripples of up to 0.4 on the Bocker Scale, could threaten the whole fabric of time. The Doctor's first visit to the station was at its inaguration, before he had left Gallifrey to become a wanderer in the fourth and fifth dimensions.

14. They had suffered a terrible catastrophe on their home planet which had been occasioned by a nuclear explosion and had left them all faceless and sterile.

15. They planned to kidnap Earthlings, minituarise them and transport them to their ship in orbit around Earth, and then assume their identities on the planet.

16. Professor Zaroff.

17. The Highlanders were the supporters of Bonnie Prince Charlie, the Young Pretender to the throne of England. The Redcoats were the supporters of King George II, the Hanoverian King of England.

18. The antiques were the property of the shop's owner, Edward Waterfield, who had brought them with him through time from Victorian England. As he himself said, 'Victorian time pieces are my specialty'!

19. At Piccadilly Circus underground station.
20. Professor Zaroff.

The Daleks and the Thals/1 – page 15

1. The fifth Doctor. His moral scruples stopped him from carrying out his task, much to Davros's relief – and disgust.
2. Spiridon.
3. The static electricity on which they depended for mobility on the Earth colony of Vulcan.
4. The Movellans won the war by developing a deadly virus which exclusively attacked Daleks. The Daleks were then forced to break up and flee to the far corners of the Universe to work on developing an antidote to the virus.
5. The DJ on Necros.
6. Three Daleks which the second Doctor implanted with the Human Factor, thereby turning them into friendly creatures with whom he played a bizarre game of 'trains'. The Human Factor also caused the Daleks to question the orders of their masters, and provoked the Dalek Civil War on Skaro.
7. Davros.
8. The planet of the Ogrons.
9. The Daleks promised to give the Thals food, in return for which the Thals would help to recultivate the land around the Dalek City. Of course this was merely a ruse to enable the Daleks to exterminate the Thals.
10. He was sentenced to further imprisonment in a cryogenic chamber on board a prison ship where he was the only prisoner. He remained there for ninety years of 'mind-numbing boredom' before he was rescued by the Daleks and Lytton.
11. The third Doctor.
12. Thal robots.
13. Kembel; Earth; Mira; Desperus; Tigus.
14. To produce a cure for the deadly Movellan disease which was affecting the Daleks. Failing that, they saw the possibility of Davros being able to somehow

genetically alter the Daleks so that they would become immune.

15. The presence of Vaaga plants on Kembel. These plants are developed in the Dalek laboratories on Skaro and are used as protective forces by the Daleks.

16. In the Space Museum on Xeros when he was being pursued by the Moroks.

17. She employed the services of Orcini to assassinate Davros. After Davros's death Orcini was to activate a transmitter which was supposedly to alert Kara of Davros's demise and enable her to mobilise her own forces to round up Davros's agents. The transmitter was, in fact, a bomb.

18. They were brought to Earth by Maxtible and Waterfield's time-travel experiments using mirrors and static electricity.

19. Lytton.

20. Two hundred years. They took over shortly after World War Three which took place in the last quarter of the twentieth century.

The Adventures of the Third Doctor/1 – page 16

1. The Master.

2. At the village of Devil's End. The Devil's Hump was believed by Professor Horner to be an ancient barrow, but actually contained Azal, the last of the Daemons on Earth, and his spacecraft.

3. He put himself into a coma to recuperate after the traumas of his regeneration, and to cure himself from the slight wound he received from a UNIT bullet.

4. The explosion was caused by a Dalekanium bomb brought from the future and which released no radiation.

5. Alpha Centauri.

6. Exarius. The Doctor, using the TARDIS console, had previously visited a parallel Earth however.

7. Professor Thascalos – in reality, the Master.

8. A particularly violent criminal whose mind was rid of all its evil by the mind parasite within the Keller Machine.

9. Their city, which then drove them out of it.

10. The *SS Bernice* which was captured and placed inside the Scope which eventually came into Vorg's possession.
11. A fellow inmate of the Doctor on the Luna Penal Colony, and a supporter of the Peace Party on Earth. He made an abortive escape attempt with the Doctor.
12. It was originally produced millions of years ago to destroy the ape-primitives who were threatening the Silurians' crops.
13. They were not the true astronauts but the Martian ambassadors wearing space suits.
14. The assistant to Professor Keller (the Master). He was killed by the Keller Machine which used the professor's fear of drowning to destroy him.
15. Sir Keith Gold.
16. The Master.
17. Those on the surface were a backward people who worshipped their city. The subterranean Exxilons, of whom Bellal and Gotal were members, lived a harassed existence underneath the planet's surface, all too painfully aware of their glorious past.
18. A pterodactyl, brought to London by Professor Whitaker's Time Scoop.
19. *Spearhead From Space*.
20. 'Close your pretty eyes, my darling; well, three of them at least.' This is an old Venusian lullaby of which Aggedor and the third Doctor were especially fond. The Doctor sang this lullaby to soothe the savage Aggedor on Peladon.

Companions of the Doctor/1 – page 18

1. She was sickened by the slaughter she had witnessed during the fifth Doctor's battle with the Daleks. The Doctor and Tegan had, of course, parted company once before, when Tegan was unwillingly left behind at Heathrow by the Doctor and Nyssa in their haste to avoid any awkward questions by that airport's authorities.
2. Barbara. She was bought in the Roman slave market by Tavius, the slave buyer of the Emperor Nero. Tavius

bought the schoolteacher because he was impressed by the kindness she had shown to a fellow prisoner.
3. Jo Grant.
4. The Brigadier, whom he also mistook for Hannibal!
5. *Vengeance on Varos*.
6. Autloc who Barbara had persuaded to question the whole morality of human sacrifice.
7. Jamie. All the others met their deaths during their travels with the Doctor.
8. The space station of Dastari.
9. Morocco for a three months' holiday with two English students she had met.
10. She refused to believe in Xoannon. The Sevateem offered her a choice between banishment and the Test of the Horda. She chose banishment although her father, Sole, took the Test of the Horda in her place.
11. The Yeti and the Sea Devils. She met the Daleks on Exxilon, the Cybermen on Gallifrey and Styre the Sontaran on the Earth of the far future.
12. In the space station's infrastructure where he was found by the sixth Doctor and Peri.
13. Ian and Barbara who were teachers at Coal Hill School, and the Brigadier who became a teacher at Brendon school after his retirement from UNIT.
14. The Doctor first met Sergeant Benton – or Corporal Benton as he then was – during his second regeneration at the time of the Cybermen invasion. By the Doctor's fourth regeneration Benton had been promoted to Regimental Sergeant Major.
15. (a) Sarah Jane Smith; (b) Romana.

The Adventures of the Fourth Doctor/1 – page 19

1. Sutekh.
2. Because Maren had secretly fed the Flame with powdered rine-weed.
3. They were slaughtered and defeated by the Gundans, and entered upon their life of slavery – just as they had formerly enslaved other creatures.
4. Kroll.

5. Garron on Ribos.
6. Romana. She journeyed there in the Nimon's travel capsule.
7. The Bi-Al Foundation, or the Centre for Alien Biomorphology. Leela took the Doctor there so he could be cured from the virus of the swarm with which he had become infected.
8. Voga. Neophobos was the name given to the mysterious asteroid which had been captured by Jupiter's gravity some fifty years before the Cybermen's attack on Nerva. Kellman renamed it Voga, realising that the asteroid was, in fact, the fabled Planet of Gold.
9. They were driven out by Humans.
10. When he was regenerated he recognised the need to assume a form acceptable to Humans, and based his appearance on the first creature he encountered, namely Sarah Jane Smith.
11. The domain of the Nimon and a constantly changing maze which was, in reality, a giant positronic circuit, capable of channelling the energy generated from hymetusite crystals to open up a Black Hole through which the Nimon creatures were able to travel from Crinoth.
12. The personal assistant to the Gatherer on Pluto. She later defied the Company and joined the rebels in liberating Megropolis One.
13. Another king would be chosen from the nobles assembled for the coronation.
14. At the end of their lives the Argolin age at a shockingly rapid rate, changing in a matter of minutes from a spry, apparently young person to a husk of a body. This is also accompanied by the falling out from their elaborate coned hair of 'seed pods'.
15. Uvanov's crew on board the Sandminer.
16. The village of Evesham which the Kraals used as a training ground. The village was, in fact, an almost perfect copy of the original on Earth.
17. The Master when he became a Melkur on Traken. 'Melkur' is a Traken world literally meaning 'a fly caught by honey'.
18. They made great use of lead panelling, lead being the

rarest metal in that empire. The Doctor had his Presidential quarters on Gallifrey built in this style to prevent the Vardans from reading his thoughts.

19. Skaro.
20. The Vampires possessed an extremely efficient cardiovascular system, enabling them to seal off any minor wounds. Only a stake through their heart could therefore destroy them.

The Adventures of the Fifth Doctor/1 – page 20

1. The deformed villain and one-time partner of Morgus who dwelt in the lower reaches of the Caves of Androzani. He was particularly adept in the construction of androids.
2. Sir George Hutchinson who became possessed by the Malus. His right-hand man was Joseph Willow.
3. Thalia introduced a pulse loop into the Matrix's Master Control, which distracted Omega long enough to allow the Doctor to leave Gallifrey undetected.
4. Davros. In the event of the station being boarded he was to be killed. However, such was the decrepit nature of the systems on board the station that, when the Daleks attacked, the mechanism to kill Davros failed to work.
5. Frontios in the Veruna System.
6. A Dalek, Cybermen, a Yeti, a Raston Warrior Robot, and the Brigadier, Sarah Jane Smith, Tegan and Turlough. The Doctors, Susan and the Master were, of course, on their home planet, and Zoe, Jamie, Liz Shaw and Mike Yates were merely apparitions conjured up to halt the Doctors' progress into the Dark Tower.
7. Kamelion under the control of the Master.
8. They are all Trion agents.
9. The Kamelion-King John on thirteenth-century Earth.
10. Manussa.
11. Urbanka. When the pollution caused by Monarch's technology destroyed that planet's protective ozone layer, the planet's surface was scorched by Inoshki's ultra-violet light.
12. One of a series of security satellites orbiting the Earth in

the twenty-first century, which attacked the TARDIS.
13. A deadly carnivorous beast lurking in the Caves of Androzani Minor.
14. The Doctor, Tegan and King John in *The King's Demons*; the Master in *The King's Demons* and *Planet of Fire*; and Professor Howard Foster, Peri's step-father, in *Planet of Fire*.
15. A living creature, re-engineered as an instrument of war and sent to Earth to pave the way for an invasion – presumably by the people of Hakol. It depended upon a massive influx of psychic energy for it to become fully activated. For some reason the planned invasion did not take place and the Malus lay dormant in the crypt of Little Hodcombe Church until it was partially re-activated in 1643 and 1984.
16. During the battle between the Cavaliers and the Roundheads in Little Hodcome Church in 1643. This was its first recorded appearance but it had evidently been laying dormant there for some time.
17. The effort required in bringing the TARDIS together again on Frontios drained all his energies. The Doctor then took him to Kolkochron where he would have only the rocks and boulders there on which to exercise his 'magnetic personality'!
18. General Chellak.
19. Greedy for knowledge, he 'sacrificed' himself to the Xeraphin and was absorbed into its life force. A manifestation of Hayter later appeared in the TARDIS and piloted the time-machine to the Inner Sanctum of Kalid's Citadel to save the Doctor.
20. Shardovan who interfered with the Master's web which held Castrovalva's existence in balance.

The Master – page 21

1. The Rani.
2. To use the regenerative properities of the numismaton gas found on that planet to return him to his proper size, after he had been minituarised in an experiment with his Tissue Compression Eliminator.

3. With a time sensor able to track down any disturbance in the time field. Jo rather prosaically referred to it as a 'TARDIS sniffer-outer'.
4. Kalid (the Master).
5. The Seal of the High Council. The third Doctor however considered it to have been either forged or stolen.
6. In the Doctor's TARDIS, into which he had materialised his own TARDIS.
7. The good and the evil of the Xeraphin were so evenly divided that the power sometimes worked for the Master and sometimes against him.
8. To make a last-ditch attempt to save the Universe from the growing entropy field which the Master had unwittingly caused by interfering with the Logopolitan Program.
9. Because in his evil undertakings, the Master had often found it necessary to regenerate much more frequently than the Doctor.
10. He had it thrown down a deep mine shaft.
11. A scarecrow.
12. He intended to use the genius of the men attending a meeting to be held by George Stephenson to establish the Earth as a power base for a successful conquest of the galaxy.
13. After saving Sir Geoffrey de Lacey from the cold embrace of the Iron Maiden, the Doctor took up the challenge to fight Sir Gilles Estram, the King's Champion – in reality, the Master.
14. He displaced the Doctor's TARDIS from the current time frame, thereby placing the TARDIS always a few seconds ahead of the Doctor.
15. Kamelion.

The Time Lords/1 – page 22

1. Chancellor Goth, who assassinated his President on the orders of the Master, who then attemped to frame the Doctor for the murder.
2. Romana, who was the Doctor's junior by several centuries. Borusa was not, of course, a student at the

Academy at the same time as the Doctor, but did teach him there.

3. A ceremonial figure in Time Lord society who officiates at the inauguration of the President.

4. The Panopticon Museum, where was also to be found a rather elegant grandfather clock – in reality the Master's TARDIS.

5. He is in charge of the Chancellery Guard, responsible for all security within the Time Lord Capitol.

6. The Rani and the second Doctor. The Rani's was very possibly her own invention, but the second Doctor was given his by the Time Lords.

7. The former Master of Jaconda, and the alias of Azmael, the Doctor's great friend and former mentor.

8. Because of her unethical experiments on animal life which, as the Master so eloquently put it, turned 'mice into monsters'. When one of her creations got out of control and even attacked the Lord President, it was decided that Gallifrey could no longer tolerate her unholy experiments.

9. The Meddling Monk.

10. A harp which, when played in the correct sequence of chords, would open a secret door leading to the Game Control Room.

11. The Castellan.

12. That a Time Lord should use all his efforts to destroy the King Vampire, even at the cost of his own life.

13. It is a powerful restorative. It also turns purple in the presence of certain gases in the Praxsis range of the spectrum, to which the Doctor is particularly allergic.

14. The marriages between Susan and David Campbell, and Leela and Andred. The Doctor, of course, became unwittingly engaged to Cameca in Mexico; and the Master set himself up as King alongside Queen Galleia in ancient Atlantis.

15. He confiscated from her her priceless brain fluid which she had collected from the Humans, and the chemically impregnated maggot-like creatures which she used to condition her human slaves. He also showed to her the interest the Doctor was taking in the extraordinary violence at Lord Ravensworth's colliery, something

which would directly affect her plans. Rather reluctantly, the Rani then joined the Master in his schemes.

The Adventures of the Sixth Doctor/1 – page 23

1. A time-travel device of the Borad's design on Karfel which was used by the Karfelons as a means of banishing undesirable persons from their society.
2. Blue. Custom on this planet also dictated that women's legs be covered at all time.
3. The energies emitted from the TARDISes of the Rani and the Master.
4. For rebelling against the accepted government of Varos, Jondar was sentenced to death by laser obliteration. After he had been saved by the Doctor he was subsequentially condemned to death by hanging, although this was a ruse on the part of the Governor to pesuade the Doctor and Jondar to co-operate.
5. Romulus and Remus. They were mathematical geniuses.
6. An Androgum and chatelaine of Dastari's space station. Dastari had operated on her nine times, technically augmenting her to such a level that she was a mega-genius. Indeed she considered herself to be among the gods.
7. She fell a victim of molecular disintegration when she attempted to escape the Doctors by operating the Kartz-Reimer time-capsule which had not been fully primed by the Doctor.
8. Vena, who had fallen into the Timelash and was travelling to nineteenth-century Earth.
9. Varos.
10. The Earth lieutenant who was dispatched to search for the missing Sylvest twins, Romulus and Remus, and helped the sixth Doctor in his battle against Mestor on Jaconda.
11. The bodies of men and women who had opted to be put into suspended animation until such time when a cure for their terminal diseases could be found; and, of course, Davros and his Daleks.
12. A fish much prized by the sixth Doctor, whose

unforgettable flavour he once extolled to Peri.

13. Apart from emitting an odour which is extremely attractive to the Morlox on Karfel, it can also precipitate tissue amalgamation between two different species. It was exposure to Mustakozene 80 which transformed the scientist Megelen into a half-Morlox/ half-Karfelon, but with an increased brainpower and a life expectancy of twelve centuries.

14. In the middle of a slag-heap on nineteenth-century Earth. The TARDIS had been diverted off-course by the Master.

15. Should the Governor pursue unpopular policies the Varosians could, by a system of referenda, choose to end the Governor's life by a cell disintegrator.

16. The giant gastropods.

17. Shockeye. When Oscar Botcherby refused to accept this method of payment the Androgum killed him.

18. Titan Three.

19. Orcini, although at that time he was 'temporarily excommunicated' from his order. He came to Necros at Kara's request – and found to his pleasure that the person he was to assassinate was Davros.

20. A scientist and one-time friend of the Doctor whose unethical experiments on the Morlox of Karfel forced the third Doctor to report him to Karfel's Inner Sanctum. Following an accident with Mustakozene 80, he became the Borad, and dictator of Karfel, until he was defeated by the sixth Doctor.

The Adventures of the First Doctor/2 – page 24

1. The Savages on Jano's world.
2. The Meddling Monk.
3. The TARDIS.
4. The dolls of the Celestial Toymaker's domain, four of whom Dodo and Steven used to determine whether the Toymaker's deadly chairs were safe or not, and three others whom they met on the Dancing Floor.
5. *The Aztecs*.
6. To the planet Astra where her father had found work.

7. An early 1960s' pop group, much loved by Susan. John Smith was the stage name of the Honourable Aubrey Waites who started off his career as Chris Waites and the Carollers.

8. Through thought transference, in a manner similar to the Sensorites' method of communication (see *The Sensorites*).

9. A mettalic mesh which isolated the Chumbley from the control waves beamed at it from the Rills' ship.

10. Jano. He could do this only by draining the life force of the Savages, the other inhabitants of his planet.

11. With the TARDIS trapped behind a fallen metal girder, the Doctor and Ian set off in search of an oxyacetylene torch, or similar cutting equipment. Barbara remained behind with Susan, who had injured her ankle.

12. Vicki.

13. In return for Ixta providing him with plans showing an entrance into the tomb in which the TARDIS was to be found, the Doctor promised to give him a poison which would help the warrior defeat his opponents, unaware that Ixta's next opponent was to be Ian!

14. Jeff Garvey and Gordon Lowery. Both became infected by Vaaga plants and were killed by Cory, who was himself exterminated by the Daleks.

15. Seth Harper.

16. The Doctor played the Trilogic Game with the Toymaker, Dodo and Steven played a bizarre and deadly game of Blind Man's Bluff with Joey and Clara; Musical Chairs with the Hearts Family; Hopscotch with Cyril the cunning schoolboy; Hunt the Key with Mrs Wigs and Sergeant Rugg; and they attempted to escape the dancing dolls on the Dancing Floor.

17. An Atmospheric Density Jacket – or ADJ – is a jacket which enables its wearer to breathe in a thinner atmosphere than that to which he is accustomed. The Doctor and Ian used ADJs on Vortis, although Vortis's atmosphere was not so thin that it was impossible to cross the planet's surface without one.

18. Fear (see *The Tribe of Gum*).

19. The Aridians lived in the underwater cities of the Sagaro Sea and the Mire Beasts lived in the slime at the ocean's

bottom.
20. The Monoids during the Doctor's second visit to the Space Ark.

Adventures in History/2 – page 25

1. George Stephenson.
2. In a baker's shop in Pudding Lane. The Doctor located the base by homing in on its electrical activity – not something one would expect to find in seventeenth-century London!
3. The crew won the Highlanders' trust when the Doctor tended the wounds of Colin McLaren, the head of the clan.
4. A beautiful flower discovered by George Cranleigh on the banks of the Orinoco river. *Black Orchid* was also the title of a book he had written.
5. That of Flavius Guiscard who was away campaigning in Gaul. Whether Flavius was known to the Doctor from a previous visit is not known.
6. Li H'sen Chang. The Eye of the Dragon was a deadly ray emitted from the eye of an ornamental dragon in Magnus Greel's lair, and used by Mr Sin in an attempt to kill the Doctor.
7. Either by knocking the Time Lord out with his six-shooter, or getting him drunk. The Doctor was horrified ...
8. The Terileptils' Android.
9. The head of the Revolution in France whom Napoleon and Paul Barras planned to overthrow.
10. His unstable mind believed her to be his former fiancée, Ann Talbot.
11. The Cult of Demnos.
12. Dalios of Atlantis.
13. They heated bamboo stalks in the fire, and the resulting explosions, together with the death of Acomat, their leader, frightened the bandits away.
14. His sonic screwdriver which was destroyed by the Terileptils' leader. It had indeed proved to be a most valuable aid ever since *Fury From The Deep*.

15. He inadvertently proposed to her by making and sharing a cup of cocoa with her. In gratitude, Cameca presented him with a brooch which had been given to her by Ixta's father. In a rare display of sentiment, the Doctor took the brooch with him when the TARDIS left Mexico.
16. She convinced the gaoler that she was an evil demon.
17. The Civil War and, in particular, one day in 1643 when a battle raged between Cavaliers and Roundheads near little Hodcombe church.
18. That battle had partially reactivated the Malus, and Sir George's recreation of that event was needed to generate sufficient psychic energy to fully reactivate the malevolent creature.
19. In a game of backgammon with Kublai Khan in which lost the TARDIS.
20. The lodestone which was the entrance to the space-time tunnel which connected the Scarman house to Sutekh's tomb in Egypt.

The Adventures of the Second Doctor/2 – page 26

1. Shockeye and the second Doctor.
2. A Yeti.
3. Salamander.
4. The Karkus in the Land of Fiction.
5. The President of the High Council of the Time Lords, who later called up the first Doctor to stop the incessant bickering of his subsequent incarnations. The Chancellor of the Time Lords was initially against this plan to defeat Omega.
6. She was able to crawl under the force field which was barring their exit from their cell, and, once outside, operate the correct sequence of buttons to deactivate the force field – a sequence she had earlier memorised.
7. Teel and Kando, who are Dulcians.
8. The planet's crust was particularly thin at this part of the planet, so making it easier for the Dominators to bore through to the planet's magma.
9. The black arm-sheaths they wore, which were linked to

the white arm-sheaths worn by the human originals.

10. A claw on the Doctor's time scanner, a device which was able to project possible future events.
11. By using his sonic gun.
12. Gia Kelly.
13. The McLaren clan's, of which Jamie was a member.
14. The people of Atlantis.
15. Packer.
16. He denied the unicorn's existence, arguing that a fictional creature could not do them any real harm.
17. Into outer space on the dark side of the Moon, where the time-machine was attacked by a missile fired from the Cybership in orbit there.
18. They were naturally adapted Atlanteans who were able to survive in the sea after the sinking of their home; and Humans, rescued from shipwrecks and operated upon by Damon. They collected food for the Atlanteans. Polly was almost turned into one of them.
19. America.
20. Zoe. After overcoming her initial amusement at the sight of Jamie's kilt, the two became firm friends.

Companions of the Doctor/2 – page 27

1. He locked his granddaughter out of the TARDIS, realising that, though she had fallen in love with David Campbell and longed to stay on Earth with him, she could never leave her grandfather of her own free will. Despite his promise that he would one day come back to visit her, they were only reunited many years later, in the Death Zone on Gallifrey, when Susan was a grown woman.
2. By realising that, as well as being English and not American as Lavinia was, Sarah Jane was far too young to be the eminent scientist.
3. Junior Ensign Commander Vislor Turlough.
4. Shockeye.
5. The first was constructed by Professor Marius who was unable to bring his pet dog with him into space. After this model of K9 elected to stay behind on Gallifrey with

Leela, the Doctor constructed an improved version of the canine computer. The third version of K9 was also made by the Doctor and given to Sarah Jane as a gift.

6. Tegan and Turlough.
7. Vicki, who was placed under the protection of Joanna, the sister of Richard the Lionheart, in twelfth-century Palestine.
8. Varsh, Adric's brother, died at the hands of the Marshmen. Sara Kingdom shot her own brother, Bret Vyon, wrongly assuming him to be a traitor.
9. They believed that her death would ensure the success of their attack upon the refinery.
10. Sharaz Jek and the Borad.
11. Barbara who was commanded to entertain Saladin. She considered telling him the tales of Hans Christian Andersen, *Romeo and Juliet* and *Gulliver's Travels*.
12. He also managed to climb down the length of cable from the Mechonoid City and stumbled into the TARDIS, presumably when the crew members were exploring the Daleks' time-machine.
13. Romana and presumably K9.
14. At the time of Borusa's attempt to achieve immortality when she was reunited with the third Doctor.
15. She claimed that she was investigating the area in the search for suitable holiday accommodation for American students.

The Cybermen/1 – page 28

1. Humans who the Cybermen could turn into Cybermen and thereby ensure the survival of their race.
2. A concoction of acetone and various other alcohols and acids which had the effect of dissolving the Cybermen's chest units on the Moonbase.
3. The Cybermen's deadly bomb which was to destroy Earth.
4. Tobias Vaughn. His body was cybernetic although his mind remained his own.
5. He led them across the death trap in the Dark Tower which resembled a large chessboard. He alone knew the

correct route to take.

6. One of the Cybermen who invaded the Snowcap Ice Base.

7. The Doctor destroyed the Cyber Fleet with the Wheel's X-Ray Laser which he powered with the TARDIS's Time Vector Generator.

8. *Attack of the Cybermen* (1985); *The Tenth Planet* (1986); *The Moonbase* (2070); *Earthshock* (2526).

9. The Cryons.

10. *Tomb of the Cybermen*; *The Wheel in Space*; *Revenge of the Cybermen*.

11. The Armageddon Convention.

12. Hobson, Benoit, Nils, Sam, Ralph, and Doctor Evans; and Jim, Bob, Charlie, Joe, Jules, Peter, Ted, Franz and John.

13. Five years. Indeed Vaughn was working with the Cybermen at the time of the Yeti invasion of London which occurred four years before the Cybermen invasion.

14. They were caused by the Cybermen using the power to activate their 'sleeping' fellows.

15. Voga, the Planet of Gold.

The Adventures of the Third Doctor/2 – page 29

1. A Raston Warrior Robot. The Doctor and Sarah Jane met one in the Death Zone on Gallifrey.

2. Kronos. Kronos the Chronivore was the real-life basis for this legend.

3. He was certainly interested in the scientific possiblities of the project; but his real interest lay in using the nuclear energy available at the project to power the TARDIS.

4. A WRN officer at the Naval Base attacked by the Sea Devils.

5. Congressman Brook.

6. He attempted to take Queen Thalira as hostage.

7. They planned to convert the nuclear energy of the Wenley Moor cyclotron into microwaves capable of destroying the Van Allen Belt. The destruction of the

Belt would then expose the planet's surface to the sun's scorching ultra-violet light.

8. It would magnetically attract and hold any would-be thieves against the side of the car. It was seen in use in Episode Two of *The Ambassadors of Death*.
9. The inner workings of Vorg's Scope.
10. Upon learning that the Ice Warriors' and Azaxyr's scheme to procure the vital trisilicate had failed, the forces of Galaxy Five quickly negotiated a peace settlement.
11. Spiridon.
12. When the Master attempted to halt UNIT's advance by calling up threats from the past using the TOMTIT machine.
13. Professor Cliff Jones, the young Welsh Nobel Prize winner she met in Llanfairfach and later married.
14. The Daemons.
15. Doctor Henderson.
16. After failing to get an accurate temporal fix on the guerillas, Jo was duped into revealing their exact location in time and space.
17. He intended to use the power of axonite in his particle reversal experiments, which he hoped would eventually lead him to the power of time-travel.
18. The mind parasite within the machine absorbed all the evil impulses in the human brain.
19. King Dalios of ancient Atlantis.
20. The assistant of Professor Stahlman at Project Inferno.

The Daleks and the Thals/2 – page 30

1. Skaro.
2. A Dalek agent who lured the Doctor into a Dalek trap on their spacecraft in *Resurrection of the Daleks*. He was a Dalek duplicate who proved to be highly unstable, a fact which the Doctor used to his advantage.
3. They intended to take him to Skaro to stand trial for his crimes against the Dalek race.
4. He planned to turn him into a Dalek.
5. The Daleks were holding his daughter Victoria hostage

in the south wing of Maxtible's house.

6. To the Civic Transport Museum in Kensington,
   London. Here they hoped to meet other members of the
   Resistance and Dortmun hoped to be able to work on
   his bomb. When they reached the Museum they found it
   deserted, although a Resistance group had recently left
   there for the South Coast.
7. Exxilon.
8. A mutant and companion of Sevrin on Skaro. He
   favoured killing Sarah Jane.
9. The Daleks used their vibrascopes.
10. They planned to recondition them to serve the Supreme
    Dalek.
11. The main Dalek force was destroyed in the blast of the
    explosion and volcano brought about by the detonation
    of the Daleks' own bomb which had been diverted on its
    way down to the Earth's core. Other Daleks were
    destroyed by rebelling Humans and the sabotaging of
    the Daleks' radio transmitter.
12. He intended to turn the Time Lord into a Dalek.
13. In a warehouse in twentieth-century London. The
    Daleks considered this to be the safest place for them.
    When the cannisters were discovered by builders, who
    were converting the warehouse into flats, they were
    naturally assumed to be unexploded bombs, and an
    army bomb disposal squad, led by Colonel Archer, was
    called in. He and the bomb squad were then duplicated,
    so providing the Daleks with a guard force who would
    raise no suspicions whatsoever on twentieth-century
    Earth.
14. During their second invasion of twenty-second-century
    Earth, and indirectly through the Master in 2540.
15. Hyperon (see *Genesis of the Daleks*).
16. Barbara who was pursued through the corridors of
    the Dalek City on Skaro and eventually captured by a
    Dalek.
17. They were the result of the recoils from the phason drills
    used by the Daleks in their underground excavations of
    the old Kaled city.
18. He claimed he needed to take Dalek tissue from them in
    order to pursue his research into the deadly Movellan

virus.

19. An old woman and her daughter, members of the Daleks' camp in Bedfordshire. The Daleks rewarded them with bread, sugar and oranges.
20. A mechanical engineer on board the space station holding Davros prisoner, who became the Kaled scientist's slave.

The Adventures of the Fourth Doctor/2 – page 31

1. Biroc the Tharil.
2. Guy Crayford. He was captured by the Kraals who convinced him that he had been deserted by Earth and used him in their attempted conquest of Earth.
3. Five huge screens, arranged circularly, in the centre of which was Meglos's underground laboratory. They were a means whereby the inestimable power of the Dodecahedron could be harnessed and magnified and focussed on any planet in the Universe – with devastating results. The Doctor sabotaged the Screens to such an extent that when Meglos attempted to use them to destroy Tigella, they backfired and annihilated Zolfa-Thura instead.
4. Cordo. The price for his father's 'Golden Death' was 117 talmars.
5. Kroll.
6. (a) Noah; (b) Vira; (c) Dune.
7. Two of Romana's fellow slaves in the excavations of the Kaled city on Skaro.
8. Once the pod has opened, the Krynoid takes over a warm-blooded creature, which becomes, in turn a fully-grown Krynoid. When the Krynoid has reached the size of, for instance, a large cathedral, it germinates and spreads its deadly seed all over the planet.
9. The Evil One – or so the Sevateem believed.
10. Eldrad.
11. He adopted the fourth Doctor's form to gain access to the Power Room where the Dodecahedron was to be found, and using his redimensioner drastically reduced the size and weight of the artefact – and walked away

with it in the palm of his hand!
12. The remains of Erato's spaceship.
13. Six, each of which had its own sun.
14. To answer a distress call.
15. K9 Mark 3. He was, of course, owned by Sarah Jane Smith.
16. They hoped that by so doing they could convince the Graf Vyna Ka of the abundancy of that valuable mineral on Ribos. They then hoped to sell the planet to the Levithian nobleman.
17. Marcus Scarman breaking into Sutekh's tomb in Egypt.
18. The Kraals.
19. Members of the Customs and Excise Service of the planet Azure. They attempted to arrest the Doctor for possession of vraxoin on board the *Empress*.
20. Morbius – or rather the brain of Morbius housed in a transparent brain case and attached to the body of a monster.

The Adventures of the Fifth Doctor/2 – page 32

1. Harmless burrowing creatures found on Frontios. They possess powerful gravitational powers but are harmless without the influence of the Gravis.
2. The Terileptils.
3. A valuable member of any military establishment whose ability to mesh his mind with that of a computer could be used to co-ordinate missile attacks. Maddox was the synch-op met by the Doctor on Sea Base Four.
4. Kurkutji, the Aborigine on board Monarch's ship. He believed Monarch was taking him to Heaven.
5. A teacher at the school in Little Hodcombe who helped the Doctor in his fight with the Malus.
6. Morgus. He was succeeded by his treacherous assistant, Krau Timmin.
7. The Doctor.
8. Because the Doctor had persuaded the fake King John to order his champion, Sir Gilles Estram, to spare Hugh's life when the boy lost in a duel to the Frenchman. Such a blow to his pride was more than the

boy could bear.

9. The sole surviving member of the great Silurian Triad who led the Silurians and the Sea Devils in their take-over of Sea Base Four in the twenty-first century. The Doctor had previously met the Silurian in their caves beneath Wenley Moor in Derbyshire.

10. Love. Monarch had little knowledge of this primitive emotion or indeed of any other sentiments: he had, in fact, banished the very concept of a soul.

11. It was recommended that hostages be taken.

12. Lon.

13. Some forty years.

14. Malkon. Turlough was also hailed as a Chosen One when it was discovered that he too carried the Misos Triangle on his arm.

15. Refined spectrox. In its raw state spectrox was a deadly poison – as the Doctor found out to his cost.

16. Rifter.

17. Entering the Matrix and asking of Omega to be assured of Tegan's safety, he made contact with the girl who – at great risk to herself – gave the Doctor valuable clues to her location in Amsterdam.

18. The Doctor, Tegan and Nyssa. It was only by jetisoning 25% of the TARDIS's interior that they could generate enough thrust to escape the hydrogen inrush. However there was no way of knowing which 25% of the TARDIS would be jettisoned.

19. Wrack's right-hand man and a fellow Eternal.

20. The brash but courageous medical officer on board the space station holding Davros prisoner. She was nearing the end of her two-year period of duty when the station was attacked by Daleks. She was later shot by Dalek troopers while attempting to destroy Davros by operating the space station's self-destruct mechanism.

The Time Lords/2 – page 33

1. According to the Doctor, a symbiotic print within the physiology of a Time Lord, which is required to prime a TARDIS before it can be used by anyone.

2. Forbidden knowledge from the Dark Time of the Time Lords. Borusa ensured that they were discovered in the possession of the Castellan, in his attmepts to frame the Castellan for the re-enactment of the Game of Rassilon. The Scrolls self-ignited before they could be examined, and the Castellan was shot supposedly while trying to escape.

3. He used Omega's own matter convertor.

4. Immortality – or rather a hideous living death throughout all eternity.

5. He sabotaged the Rani's TARDIS, adjusting her navigation and velocity regulators, thereby sending her TARDIS to the far reaches of the Universe. The time spillage, inadvertently caused by the Doctor's sabotage, also caused one of the Rani's embyonic Tyrannosaurus Rexes to grow and threaten her and the Master.

6. The Minyans.

7. The third Doctor with Sarah Jane entered the Tower from the air; the second Doctor and the Brigadier passed through the system of tunnels underneath the Tower; and the first Doctor and Tegan chose to enter by the front door. The fifth Doctor, Tegan and Susan also made their way to the Tower on foot, but the girls were forced to retreat to the safety of the TARDIS when attacked by Cybermen, and the Doctor was transported to the Capitol buildings.

8. Omega located the curve of the Arc of Infinity in Amsterdam, which was above sea-level, to maintain pressure and ensure the efficient working of the fusion booster which he had stolen from Gallifrey.

9. The Master.

10. When the fifth Doctor regenerated into the sixth Doctor.

11. They sent the Doctor to defeat the Cybermen.

12. They feared that their experiments could endanger the whole fabric of time, and dispatched the second Doctor to convince Dastari that the experiments should be halted until the Gallifreyans could convince themselves of the safety factor of the time experiments.

13. Azmael. At the end of their drinking bout Azmael fell into the fountain! This Time Lord later sacrificed his

life to defeat Mestor.

14. More Time Lord Presidents have come from the Prydonian Chapter than all the other Chapters put together. One of the most prominent Presidents of the Time Lords has been the Doctor who is also a Prydonian.

15. Each time he entered the Matrix the Doctor must have been somehow linked to the mind of Rassilon, but he first saw a visual manifestation of the greatest of all Time Lords in the Dark Tower on Gallifrey.

The Adventures of the Sixth Doctor/2 – page 34

1. Bandril. They declared war on Karfel when the Borad deliberately broke the two planets' treaty of co-operation which ensured guaranteed supplies of grain to the famine-stricken Bandril.

2. One of the finest agronomists in the galaxy whose supposed 'death' brought the Doctor to Necros. Davros began to turn the professor into a Dalek until he was destroyed by his daughter, Natasha.

3. Stike.

4. Hidden 'mines', planted by the Rani and capable of transforming animal into vegetable matter – living men into trees.

5. Varos.

6. Azmael's Jacondan lieutenant who felt affection towards the Sylvest twins. He was used and finally killed by Mestor.

7. Necros.

8. Plain-clothes officers from Interpol on the trail of dangerous criminals.

9. H.G. Wells's adventures with the sixth Doctor on Karfel.

10. Mestor.

11. It was dedicated to peaceful scientific research. Some of the scientients on board included Dastaria, Kartz and Reimer.

12. Two humanoids on Telos who had been partially transformed into Cybermen. Learning of the Cyber-

men's plans to destroy Telos they planned to leave the planet in the Cybermen's stolen time-vessel which was to be found in Cyber Control. They planned to infiltrate the Base by posing as a Cyberman and prisoner.

13. It was the scrapyard belonging to I.M. Foreman at 76 Totter's Lane – the very same scrapyard where the first Doctor met Ian and Barbara in 1963.

14. The Rani.

15. Bodysnatchers who infiltrated the catacombs of Necros to investigate the supposed death of Stengos, Natasha's father. Grigory, Natasha's partner, was a doctor – and a drunkard.

16. Andromeda; he also suggested taking his American friend to the Eye of Orion which he had visited in his fifth incarnation with Tegan and Turlough.

17. A pioneer of genetic experiments and Head of Research on Space Station J7. He was a tremendously gifted scientist, and formulated the theory of parallel matter; rather like the Doctor, he detested computers. His proudest achievement was the technical augmentation of the Androgum Chessene, and he assisted her in her evil schemes. However, after being disgusted by the sight of her reverting to her basest desires, he saw the error of his ways, and was killed by his creation, shortly after he had reconciled himself with the second Doctor.

18. Savage creatures which inhabit the tunnels of the Citadel on Karfel.

19. On payment of an additional fee he 'entertained' the bodies lying in suspended animation on Necros. He was killed by a Dalek.

20. The Borad which the Doctor thought he had destroyed was, in reality, a cloned copy of the real Borad.

The Adventures of the First Doctor/3 – page 35

1. The Animus lay directly over the magnetic pole of Vortis. It was therefore able to use the planet's magnetic energy as a source of power – in fact a source of power so great that it attracted several moons into Vortis's orbit, and dragged the TARDIS off course.

2. The guards on Jano's world and in particular Captains Edal and Exorse.
3. Earth. As Maitland and Carol revealed to Ian and Barbara in *The Sensorites*, London, as the teachers knew it, had ceased to exist in the twenty-fourth century (some 400 years previously). The whole of South-East England had by that time become one vast Central City.
4. A chessboard pattern on the floor of the entrance hall which became a death trap upon reaching the fifth row of squares.
5. WOTAN, in response to a question set it by Dodo.
6. They were servitors whose duties included patrolling the Ark's forest and the maintenance and piloting of the great ship. By the Doctor's second visit the status quo on the Ark had changed dramatically and the Monoids had become the masters of the Ark.
7. An astronaut on board Captain Maitland's ship which was in orbit around the Sense Sphere. She was the fiancée of John, a fellow astronaut who had lost his mind.
8. To a rather eventful holiday in Rome!
9. Xeros.
10. *Planet of Giants*, in which the time-travellers were minituarised.
11. The Animus on Vortis.
12. She attempted to use the TARDIS to escape the planet, but failed by seconds to reach the time-machine before the Doctor.
13. Doc Holliday and the Doctor.
14. The chairs used in the bizarre game of Musical Chairs played by Dodo, Steven and the Hearts Family in the Celestial Toymaker's domain. All the chairs, save one, were deadly and to proceed on their journey and regain the security of the TARDIS it was necessary for Dodo or Steven to sit on the one safe chair. Using dolls, they eliminated the first four chairs which destroyed the dolls by crushing, electrocution, spinning the victim off into space, and dematerialisation. Dodo almost froze to death on the fifth chair but the concentrated willpower of herself and Steven saved her. The King and Queen of Hearts tried the sixth chair which smothered and

dissolved them.
15. The Sensorites.
16. General Cutler's.
17. A Zarbi, tamed by the Doctor and Vicki on Vortis.
18. Hilda was the local telephone operator whose husband, Bert, was the village constable. The voices of the miniaturised time-travellers were so high that Hilda was unable to hear them.
19. The Time Rotor.
20. This was the name by which the Optera knew the Animus on Vortis.

Adventures in History/3 – page 36

1. (a) King Richard the Lionheart; (b) Saphadin, the brother of Saladin.
2. Paris, Hector, Cassandra and Troilus.
3. The body of Marcus Scarman which was animated by the Destroyer.
4. Tegana.
5. After his attempt to kill Kublai Khan failed he killed himself.
6. The abduction from King Menelaus by Paris of Queen Helen. The Greeks declared war on the Trojans to reclaim their Queen. The great war ended when the Trojans took into their city a great wooden horse which, unknown to them, was full of Greeks – an idea suggested by the Doctor!
7. Scarlioni himself, in his true form as Scaroth of the Jagaroth.
8. He confiscated the TARDIS keys and hid them in the binding of his diary.
9. The Meddling Monk.
10. Kal.
11. Ramlah.
12. Osiran service robots.
13. Rebellious workers who, during the early days of the Industrial Revolution, destroyed the machines which they believed would deprive them of their jobs. The Doctor and Peri met several in *The Mark of the Rani*.

14. They held Isabella, his wife, prisoner.
15. The Doctor, when part of the Mandragora Helix hijacked the TARDIS and took it to Earth.
16. Ling-Tau, a courier of Kublai Khan, who rode over three hundred miles in one day, in order to escort Marco Polo's party to the Khan.
17. The galley boy of Captain Avery.
18. The Doctor.
19. A printed circuit from the control panel the Terileptils used to rule their human slaves. Nyssa was rather concerned about the consternation its discovery might cause among future archaeologists.
20. The prominent germinologist whom the Doctor sought out in the Paris of 1572 and helped to flee to Germany from the Massacre of the Protestants by the French Huguenots.

The Adventures of the Second Doctor/3 – page 38

1. Travers.
2. She set up a false homing beacon, the signal from which led the Martian invasion force into orbit around the sun and ultimate destruction.
3. *The Space Pirates.* Alpha-Four was one of the beacons used by spacecraft as a navigation aid across the vast emptiness of space. Attacked by Caven's pirates, the beacon was separated into eight pieces and steered to the planet Lobos. The TARDIS and its crew were in two different sections and, in an attempt to electromagnetically bring the two sections together, the Doctor succeeded in shooting the unit, in which he, Jamie and Zoe were, into deep space, where they finally met up with Milo Clancey.
4. When Jamie and Zoe recognised himself and the Brigadier he realised that they must be illusions. The Time Lords had returned his two companions to Earth and erased all their memories of their time with the Doctor, except for their first meeting. So, while Jamie and Zoe could have recognised the Time Lord from Culloden or the Wheel, there was no way whatsoever

that they could have recognised the Brigadier.

5. Chessene and Shockeye.
6. The proprietor of a private museum in which was to be found a deactivated Yeti, brought back from Tibet by Professor Travers. Dismissing Travers's fears that the Yeti might come back to life, he was killed by his own exhibit.
7. The Chief of Police of the colony attacked by the Macra Terror.
8. The Dominators on Dulkis.
9. Jamie was employed as a guard, Victoria as a kitchen assistant.
10. Genetic material was taken from Shockeye and introduced into the Doctor. However a second operation was needed to make the change permanent.
11. UNIT had been watching the activities of International Electromatix for some months, and the Brigadier recognised photographs of his two friends, taken when they visited the complex.
12. He launched a shower of copper needles which confused his pursuers' tracking systems.
13. The International Space Corps. General Hermack.
14. He answered more questions!
15. Polly, with Kirsty, in *The Highlanders*.
16. He used the hair of the Princess Rapunzel as a rope. Rather disturbed at Jamie's tugging at her hair, the Princess was even more outraged to discover that he was, in fact, a piper – and not a prince, as he was supposed to be!
17. Rago. Toba was the Probationer.
18. Theodore Maxtible's house which was later destroyed by the Daleks.
19. He planned to blow up the planet Ta. The Doctor defused the pirate's bomb, and Caven and his ship were destroyed by General Hermack's Minnows.
20. Jamie.

Behind the Scenes/1 – page 39

1. It was delayed for ten minutes because of a news report

on the assassination of President Kennedy.

2. (a) Robert Holmes; (b) Robert Holmes; (c) Pip and Jane Baker.

3. (a) Barry Letts; (b) John Wiles; (c) Graham Williams; (d) John Nathan-Turner; (e) Innes Lloyd; (f) Peter Bryant; (g) Derrick Sherwin; (h) Verity Lambert; (i) Philip Hinchcliffe.

4. Rather inappropriately, the first episode of *The Faceless Ones*!

5. *The Caves of Androzani*, in the last few seconds.

6. Kit Pedler.

7. Jim Dale, for the part of the third Doctor.

8. Fraser Hines and, when Hines was ill with chicken pox, Hamish Wilson for one episode of *The Mind Robber*.

9. Eleanor Bron, who played an art critic in *City of Death* and later reappeared as Kara in *Revelation of the Daleks*.

10. *Golden Death – The Daleks' Master Plan*; *Death of a Spy – The Myth Makers*; *A Land of Fear – The Reign of Terror*; *Inferno – The Romans*; *The Hall of Dolls – The Celestial Toymaker*; *The Death of Time – The Chase*.

11. The sixth Doctor, of course, and Maxil, the Gallifreyan guard who shot down the fifth Doctor in *Arc of Infinity*.

12. (a) *State of Decay*; (b) *The Sontaran Experiment*; (c) *Full Circle*; (d) *Earthshock*; (e) *Resurrection of the Daleks*; (f) *State of Decay*; (g) *Genesis of the Daleks*.

13. John Nathan-Turner, who became the show's producer in 1980.

14. Patrick Troughton. He has not co-starred with Tom Baker.

15. *The Web of Fear*.

16. Robert Holmes.

17. A one-off play submitted to the BBC which, after some rewriting, was adapted for *Doctor Who* and became known as *The Krotons*.

18. Laurence Payne. He returned to play Dastari in *The Two Doctors*.

19. *An Unearthly Child/The Tribe of Gum*; *The Krotons*; *Carnival of Monsters*; *The Three Doctors*; *Logopolis*.

20. They created the idea for the show, and guided it through its early days.

1. Mondas, the home planet of the Cybermen which was fitted with a propulsion unit which enabled it to roam the Universe.
2. They turned the Wheel's atmosphere into one of pure ozone. This plan was foiled when the Wheel switched over to its emergency supply, with which the Cybermen could not tamper.
3. Zoe and Isobel Watkins – hotly pursued by Jamie.
4. It attacks the nervous system, hence the lines visible on a victim's face which trace the course of the nerves under the skin.
5. (a) As a device projecting a hypnotic beam; (b) As a valuable addition to a Cyberman's firepower.
6. A rival band of archaeologists come to explore the Tombs of the Cybermen.
7. They planned to turn them into Cybermen.
8. Apart from the Doctor posing a threat to his plans, Vaughn intended to use the TARDIS to escape from the Cybermen, should they attempt to betray him.
9. A weapon invented by the Humans and which proved crucial in their victory over the Cybermen. It coated the Cybermen with a layer of gold.
10. In the fifteen hundred silos in the freighter's hold.
11. Commander Lytton.
12. It was on a thirty-year assignment acting as a space beacon to guide inward-bound craft past a new asteroid (Voga) which had appeared near Jupiter and whose position was not yet marked on star charts.
13. They went into hibernation to rest and recharge themselves – their race had in fact become very weak. They chose Telos because it gave them the opportunity of exploiting the Cryons' expertise at building refrigerated cities.
14. It sent out gravity beams at Earth, which influenced the tides and in turn the weather on the planet.
15. Five hundred years.

1. Humans from Earth.
2. Mutters Spiral, also known as the Milky Way.
3. Type Forty TARDISes. The discrepancy was due, of course, to the Doctor's stealing a Type Forty in his flight from Gallifrey.
4. (a) Xoanon; (b) Logar; (c) Ti; (d) Amdo; (e) Orb.
5. TARDISes.
6. The fourth Doctor.
7. The Dalek Emperor whom he met for the first and only time during his second incarnation on Skaro. The first Doctor and the Celestial Toymaker had met sometime before the Time Lord's visit with Dodo and Steven to his Toyroom, and indeed he fully expected that he would eventually meet the malevolent magician again; the Doctor and Icthar met in the Silurian caves in Derbyshire and later on Sea Base Four; the Doctor first met the Borad during his third incarnation, when the future ruler of Karfel was known as Megelen.
8. In *The Romans*, *Masque of Mandragora* and in *City of Death* when he briefly travelled from Paris to that country to meet Leonardo da Vinci.
9. The second Doctor.
10. (a) the Seeker; (b) Miss Hawthorne; (c) Granny Tyler.
11. He first witnessed the Earth's destruction some ten million years in the future on board the Space Ark, when the Earth finally plunged into the sun. He also saw the planet's destruction during his third incarnation when the forces released by Project Inferno rent the parallel Earth asunder.
12. The TARDIS scanners are surveying the outside surroundings.
13. In his shoes!
14. (a) Richard Mace; (b) Shakespeare; (c) Oscar Botcherby; (d) 'Professor' Clegg; (e) Li H'sen Chang.
15. (a) The doomed planet in Galaxy Four; (b) Aridius and the planet of the Gonds; (c) Pluto.

1. As a result of a great space plague, they had become particularly wary of all aliens.
2. Chin Lee.
3. The government of the parallel Earth in *Inferno*. Lethbridge-Stewart and Elizabeth Shaw were members of that republic's security force.
4. They claimed that their credentials were lost in the crash of their space shuttle. They also blamed the lateness of their arrival on this fact. As Jo rather pertinently remarked, the pilot was most inefficient!
5. He hoped to capture a dinosaur and surround it in an electrical field. When the dinosaur returned to its own time, he would be able to track the energy needed for such a transference back to its source.
6. He arranged for Vorn, Varan's son, to kill the Administrator presiding over the Conference. In such a situation he could then quite legitimately place Solos under his martial law.
7. Following the Doctor's instructions, relayed to her via the TARDIS's telepathic circuits, she operated an 'Extreme Emergency' control which succeeded in rematerialising the Doctor inside the TARDIS console room.
8. It could generate a fierce heat beam, kill or stun, and operate simple mechanical devices, such as locks.
9. Because he held them responsible for the death of Jim Daniels, one of his fellow crewmembers on a previous Mars flight, who died just by touching one of the aliens. Carrington truly believed that the aliens could never live in harmony with the people of Earth.
10. A drilling consultant called in by Sir Keith Gold at Project Inferno.
11. It was intended to dump the missile into the sea.
12. Because the Scope's importation broke the Inter Minoran law expressly forbidding the mass transportation of all unscrutinised alien life forms to their planet. The Inter Minorans' Eradicator had little effect on the creatures within the Scope however.
13. Aggedor, the Royal Beast of Peladon.

14. Alpha Centauri.
15. Until the planet's independence, the Overlords, or Earthmen, led by the Marshal on board Skybase One.
16. She was put into the cave of Queen Galleia and her handmaiden, Lakis.
17. The Master, posing as a special commissioner from Sirius Four, and claiming that the Doctor was a dangerous criminal who had to be returned to Sirius Four for punishment.
18. He suspected that they intended to colonise Peladon, as they once had attempted to do on Earth.
19. 31 March and the greatest occult festival of the calendar, second only to Hallowe'en. It was on this night that Professor Horner unwittingly released Azal.
20. Chairman Mao Tse-Tung.

The Adventures of the Fourth Doctor/3 – page 44

1. He was investigating a possible art fraud, and, in fact, suspected the Doctor and Romana to be part of Scarlioni's conspiracy.
2. The refinery was a methane refinery which produced the protein needed to feed the inhabitants of Delta Magna.
3. He wanted his planet to trade its valuable gold with other planetary powers.
4. Count Grendel and Madame Lamia who sent a death-dealing android double of Romana to kill the Time Lord.
5. Erato, the Tythonian ambassador to Chloris.
6. To investigate the mysterious power fluctuations in the Dodecahedron.
7. Princess Astra; Merak.
8. It was devastated by Morbius and his fanatical followers.
9. A peasant leader on the Great Vampire's planet.
10. The temporary reversion of Nature to its destructive chaos of earthquakes, fierce storms and the like which continues until the new Keeper assumes his position.
11. Lowe, the Chief Supervisor of the Titan Base. After he triggered the distress call he finally succumbed to his

mental battle with the virus of the Swarm. Leela took him to the Bi-Al Foundation where he spread his deadly infection. He was killed by K9.

12. An executive in charge of PCM production on Pluto. He later helped to liberate his people from the rule of the Company.

13. Blood.

14. The Citadel of the Oracle – or, more properly, the P7E – in which were to be found the Race Banks of the Minyan people. The Tree of Life was, in fact, the tunnel system of the Underworld, and the dragons a security device protecting the P7E.

15. The Company is a vast Usurian conglomerate which attempts to take over the galaxy by economic rather than military means. The Company's representative on Pluto was the Collector, who was liquidated by the Doctor. Like many bureaucratic organisations the Company had extensive files, including one on the Doctor and Gallifrey – in fact at one time the Company even considered developing Gallifrey.

16. The Doctor, who hoped to exhaust the Sontaran in one-to-one combat, and thereby force the Sontaran to recharge himself in his ship which Harry had sabotaged.

17. Tara. 'George' was the name the Doctor rather disrespectfully gave to the android double of Prince Reynart.

18. Morbius was unaffected as Solon had given him the lungs of a Birastrop which had an inbuilt filter.

19. A member of the Minyan crew searching for the P7E.

20. The Master's TARDIS.

The Daleks and the Thals/3 – page 45

1. They intended the Doctor's duplicate to travel to Gallifrey and assassinate the members of the High Council. The duplicates of Tegan and Turlough were meant to reinforce the deception and allay any suspicions that a Doctor travelling alone might cause.

2. Venus.

3. They researched into ways of ensuring the survival of their race.

4. He presumed that their first encounter with the Daleks had taken place many years in the future.
5. Orcini, using Kara's bomb. He also died in the explosion but he failed to destroy Davros.
6. Stien.
7. Because the Humans had condemned him to a living death in cryogenic suspension.
8. The first Doctor visited Skaro with Ian, Barbara and Susan; the second Doctor believed he had witnessed the final end of the Daleks in *Evil of the Daleks*; and the fourth Doctor twice visited Skaro, witnessing the birth of the Daleks and the creatures' return to the planet to resurrect Davros.
9. He planned to operate on their brains, making them subservient to his plans.
10. She intended to activate the prison station's self-destruct system, and almost completed her task before she was killed by the Dalek troopers.
11. A member of a bomb squad on twentieth-century Earth who was called in to investigate a hidden cache of bombs in a London warehouse. The 'bombs' were in fact cannisters of the deadly Movellan virus, and Colonel Archer and his men were destroyed and Dalek duplicates took their place.
12. Davros.
13. By a virus which affected the cables in their electrical systems (see *Genesis of the Daleks*).
14. Sarah Jane Smith. She contracted the poisoning by being forced to load the nosecone of the Thals' rocket with distronic explosives.
15. (a) A companion of Stien who escaped to twentieth-century Earth via the Daleks' time corridor, but was shot down dead by a Dalek trooper; (b) A member of the Marine Space Corps on Exxilon who sacrificed himself in destroying the Daleks on that planet. Galloway's entire family had been killed by the Daleks.

The Adventures of the Fifth Doctor/3 – page 46

1. A creature of the blackest depths of the ocean, whose biology had been tampered with by the Silurians. It

possessed immense strength and generated a powerful electrical charge, but had a great aversion to light.

2. He was incarcerated by Sir George Hutchinson after his investigations into the legend of the Malus had led him to discover the truth about the creature and Sir George's plans.

3. The Chief Elder of the Sarns.

4. To use their extraordinary gravitational powers to move Frontios around the galaxy in search of more planets to colonise and use as breeding grounds.

5. A mobile machine, used by the people of the Dome on Deva Loka for exploring their environment. It was controlled directly by the brain of its wearer. The Kinda also constructed a primitive version of the TSS for Aris, in the mistaken belief that it would offer him protection during their attack on the Dome.

6. Controller Nilson and Doctor Solow.

7. Morgus was responsible for Jek's deformity. Many years before the Doctor and Peri's visit to Androzani Minor, Jek and Morgus had been partners, Morgus providing the financial backing for Jek to design and construct the android task force which collected and refined the valuable spectrox. But eager to have all the profits from this enterprise for himself, Morgus engineered Jek's death in a mud burst. Jek, however, escaped but was horribly disfigured.

8. Mawdryn's appearance was so badly burnt and disfigured that the girls assumed that the Time Lord had been seriously injured in the journey to Earth via Mawdryn's transmat capsule. When Mawdryn regained his true form, the scientist still maintained that he was the Doctor, claiming that the transmat capsule had caused a 'mutative catalysis', causing him to regenerate into an 'alien'. The Brigadier and Nyssa allowed him the benefit of the doubt. Tegan, however, hotly disputed Mawdryn's assertion.

9. Captain Revere. He was succeeded by his son, Plantaganet.

10. Because of its controls being linked with the alien technology of the Cybermen.

11. Monarch's belief that he could travel faster than light

and thereby go past the Big Bang and meet himself –
God.

12. Adric, imprisoned in the Portreeve's (the Master's) web.
13. When the Cybermen's androids attacked both his own
    party *and* the time-travellers.
14. The people of Hakol.
15. The leader of the gun-runners encountered by the
    Doctor and Peri on Androzani Minor.
16. Periodic emissions of super-heated mud from the core of
    Androzani Minor which occur when the planet's orbit
    takes it into close proximity with its twin planet,
    Androzani Major.
17. A gas, issuing from the heart of the Fire Mountain on
    Karn, which has astonishing healing qualities.
18. Commander Vorshak; Controller Nilson; Lieutenants
    Bulic, Preston and Karina; Doctor Solow; and Maddox
    the Synch-Op. Maddox replaced Michaels as Synch-
    Op.
19. The Snakedancers, of whom Dojjen was one. The
    Doctor also danced the Dance of the Snake with Dojjen.
20. He feared that the President suspected his dealings with
    the gun-runners on Androzani Minor.

Companions of the Doctor/3 – page 47

1. Tegan. Sir George Hutchinson intended Tegan's fate to
   be that of Little Hodcombe's Queen of the May in 1643 –
   death at the burning stake.
2. Dodo in Tombstone.
3. (a) Gallifrey; (b) Trion; (c) Earth; (d) Traken; (e)
   Alzarius; (f) Gallifrey.
4. K9 and Kamelion. Strictly speaking, the Doctor had
   three robotic companions as there were two models of
   K9 which travelled with him.
5. Leela in *The Invisible Enemy*.
6. Donald McLaren who was also a piper, as was his
   father.
7. She opened up one of the 'spaceship's' exit hatches, and
   showed Mark the world outside.
8. Adric.

9. A Trion agent.
10. They planned to prove her mortality by poisoning her. Barbara saw through Tlotoxl's deceit and even admitted to the High Priest of Sacrifice that she was not divine – and defied him to prove it!
11. (a) Vanessa; (b) Colin Fraser; (c) Andrew Verney.
12. Ten years. The Black Guardian promised to liberate him if he killed the Doctor. He returned to Trion with his brother, Malkon, after he discovered that the persecution of the Imperial Clans had long since ended.
13. *The Mind Robber*. Attacked by a Redcoat, Jamie was turned into a cardboard cut-out and the Doctor then given the task of re-assembling the Highlander's face from a board of jigsaw-like pieces. With typical clumsiness the Doctor gave his young friend the wrong face!
14. Turlough.
15. Polly and Ben witnessed the Doctor's first regeneration; Sarah Jane and the Brigadier saw the Time Lord's third regeneration; the fifth Doctor would probably not have survived if not for the presence of Tegan, Adric and Nyssa; and Peri witnessed the transformation of the Doctor into his sixth incarnation. The Doctor's second regeneration was seen by nobody except, perhaps, the Time Lords.

The Adventures of the Sixth Doctor/3 – page 48

1. To obtain Zeiton 7 ore, without which the TARDIS was incapable of further travel through time and space.
2. Shockeye o' the Quawncing Grig and Chessene o' the Franzine Grig.
3. In a bathhouse, although her TARDIS had originally materialised in a mine shaft.
4. Anita.
5. The Doctor's curiosity which had been aroused by the fact that his friend Arthur Stengos had apparently chosen to be put into suspended animation on the planet, rather than calmly accepting death.
6. Scotland in 1179. When Vena entered the Timelash she

116

was transported to 1885, owing to the TARDIS's interference with the machine.

7. Tekker (who had succeeded Renis), and Mykros.
8. Zeiton 7, a valuable ore, essential as a power source for all the galaxy's space and time ships. The Galatron Mining Corporation was offering the Varosians the miserable sum of seven credits per unit at the time of the sixth Doctor's arrival on that planet. Varos also made some revenue out of the entertainment and communications industry, selling videotapes of their frequent tortures and executions to all 'civilised' races in the galaxy.
9. He communicated telepathically with his other self. The ringing of the Santa Maria Bell at Seville's cathedral helped him to fix the location of the dungeon where he was being held.
10. Jabel. He was a highly talented embalmer but also an incorrigible philanderer, and was killed by his student Tasambeker, whose affections he had constantly spurned.
11. The husband of the woman who Jabel was embalming at the time of the sixth Doctor's arrival on Necros.
12. Shockeye.
13. To spare himself the sight of his own deformed appearance. Mirrors also seemed to have a disorientating effect on the Borad's androids.
14. Members of Amol, a rival mining corporation.
15. A third year student of Jabel on Necros, of whom she was particularly fond. Her love was however unreciprocated and, acting under Davros's orders, she killed her teacher. She was then exterminated by Davros's Daleks.
16. The Cryons on Telos.
17. The Doctor tried to repair the circuit after leaving Jaconda and met with some limited success. The timemachine changed its appearance three times – into an ornate wardrobe, an organ and a huge set of double doors set into the walls of the Cyber Tombs on Telos – before settling down into the familiar shape of a London police box.
18. Varl.

19. Oscar Botcherby.
20. A mineral common in the colder areas of Telos. It is highly unstable and at a temperature of 15° above freezing it self-ignites.

The Adventures of the First Doctor/4 – page 49

1. A dance floor, at the end of which lay a fake TARDIS. Dodo and Steven were set the task of crossing the dance floor and avoiding the embrace of the dancing dolls who would attempt to dance with them for all eternity. The key to the door which led to the Floor was hidden in an apple pie in Mrs Wiggs's kitchen.
2. One of the seven participants in the Daleks' Master Plan.
3. Ian and Barbara. They imprisoned the real innkeeper in the inn's cellar.
4. At the time of his first visit they used sign language; they later developed artificial voice boxes.
5. They had all been infected with the deadly insecticide, DN6.
6. The time-machine generated a force directly opposite to the force wielded by the Animus who controlled the Zarbi.
7. Rheumatism.
8. Because the TARDIS lock had been stolen by the Sensorites.
9. Two clowns who challenged Dodo and Steven to a deadly game of Blind Man's Bluff in the domain of the Celestial Toymaker.
10. Darcy Tranton in *The Feast of Steven*.
11. Jano's people.
12. Most of the Humans were miniuarised and carried within microcells.
13. Quite appropriately in the People's Hall of Judgement.
14. Its dark side.
15. It needed the Astral Map to discover the location of the Menoptera forces who were preparing to invade and reclaim the planet.
16. The time-machine had materialised on Captain Mait-

land's ship which was in orbit around the Sense Sphere.
17. Drahva.
18. A merchant from Jaffa, from whose selection of clothes the Doctor chose garments suitable for twelfth-century Palestine.
19. The Beatles playing *Ticket to Ride*!
20. A gas used by the Moroks in their attempts to defeat the rebels on Xeros.

The Adventures of the Second Doctor/4 – page 50

1. She joined forces with him to help in the salvaging of space flotsam. By the time she discovered Caven's true intentions she was too deeply involved to pull out.
2. The full force of the explosion was absorbed by the cobweb, with which a Yeti had encased the pack of explosives.
3. He challenged him to a duel. Stike, however, declined, as the Doctor was not a Sontaran.
4. He used the Sun Store to focus the sun's rays on barren and infertile areas of the globe, thereby encouraging the cultivation of food plants.
5. It intended to bring all of Earth's inhabitants to the Land of Fiction and then to use their creative powers to extend its domain into the world of reality.
6. A Tibetan holy bell. The monks of the Det-Sen monastery once entrusted the Doctor with the safe-keeping of one.
7. The Dominators had absorbed the radiation in their attempts to power their ship.
8. She ended the partnership after the disappearance of her father. She believed Milo Clancey to have been responsible for his murder.
9. They were the servitors on board the station.
10. He shielded her from the effects of the dispersion unit with his umbrella.
11. The Krotons.
12. He intercepted the Dominators' seed device on its way down to Dulkis's core, and planted it on board the Dominators' ship – with explosive results!

13. The first Doctor in *The Three Doctors*.
14. Vaughn's rate of blinking was very much slower than that of a normal Human.
15. The creative energy of the elderly Master of that land.
16. An insular protest group on Earth, of which Jamie was briefly suspected of being a member on the Wheel in Space.
17. The second Doctor (although Jamie believed he had seen him killed) and Jamie. Chessene, Shockeye and Dastari, who had been accesories to the massacre, also left the space station alive.
18. Small fighter and pursuer space ships.
19. He followed the example of Perseus, and foiled the Gorgon's plan by looking at her reflection in a mirror. She was then unable to turn the Doctor and Zoe to stone, but became stone herself.
20. The clerk of the crooked Solicitor Grey, who later accompanied the Highlanders to France acting as a secretary and interpreter.

Who Said What? – page 52

1. The first Doctor talking to an incredulous Ian in *The Tribe of Gum*.
2. The Great One in the insane moments before her death in *Planet of Spiders*.
3. Nyssa, speaking of the Master's destruction of her family and home planet in *Logopolis*.
4. The fourth Doctor, praising the human species to Harry, in *The Ark in Space*.
5. The proud chant of the Daleks entombed in Davros's bunker on Skaro, shortly after 'exterminating' their creator in *Genesis of the Daleks*.
6. The fourth Doctor in *Revenge of the Cybermen* after Harry had caused a rockfall and was about to remove the booby-trapped Cyberbomb from the Doctor's unconscious body.
7. The second Doctor in a heart-to-heart speech to Victoria in *The Tomb of the Cybermen*, and shortly after he had explained to the girl that, though he loved

his family, most of the time they 'slept' in his mind and he forgot about them.

8. Shardovan to the Master in *Castrovalva*, shortly before he destroyed the evil Time Lord's web which was keeping Castrovalva in existence.

9. Davros, explaining to the Doctor how his Daleks would bring peace to the Universe, in *Genesis of the Daleks*.

10. Susan explaining her origins to a disbelieving Barbara and Ian in *An Unearthly Child*.

11. Omega, bemoaning his imprisonment in the anti-matter universe, in *The Three Doctors*.

12. Icthar outlining his plans for humanity in *Warriors of the Deep*.

13. The fourth Doctor debating the morality involved in destroying the Daleks in *Genesis of the Daleks*.

14. A dismayed Brigadier in *The Three Doctors*.

15. Tegan in *The Visitation* when the Doctor had once again failed to take her to Heathrow Airport.

16. The Black Guardian, reminding Turlough of the promise he made him, in *Mawdryn Undead*.

17. Lord President Borusa, revealing his reasons for seeking immortality, in *The Five Doctors*.

18. Chessene, revealing the full extent of her ambitions, in *The Two Doctors*.

19. Tobias Vaughn, dismayed at the Cybermen's betrayal of him, and explaining his motives to the second Doctor in *The Invasion*.

20. One of the Cybermen, explaining the 'superiority' of his race to the Humans, in *The Moonbase*.

The Adventures of the Third Doctor/4 – page 53

1. A rocky area on the planet. The boulders found there absorb solar heat by day and release it at night. The Doctor, Jo and their Thal friends sheltered there, surrounded by the wild animals of Spiridon.

2. That a planet's holy laws may not be interfered with by Federation members. The delegates were therefore unable to help the Doctor when he was condemned to death by Hepesh for defiling the Inner Sanctum of the

Temple of Aggedor. Jo did appeal to King Peladon however, and Peladon decreed that the Doctor should submit himself to trial by combat instead.

3. Harry Slocum.

4. A race of awesomely powerful creatures who actually feed on time and live outside the bounds of time and space. Their leader is Kronos.

5. The leader of the Chinese delegation to the international peace conference who replaced the murdered General Cheng Teik. The third Doctor's mastery of the Hokkein dialect of Chinese instantly endeared the Time Lord to the diplomat.

6. The atmosphere of the planet was poisonous to Humans.

7. The secretary of Sir Reginald Styles.

8. He was finally convinced when a captured 'Earthman' was transformed before his own eyes into an Ogron, thus proving the truth of the Doctor's claims.

9. General Carrington.

10. Some 3,500 years ago in the vaults of the Temple of Poseidon in ancient Atlantis. It was guarded by the Minotaur.

11. Axonite.

12. Because his mind possessed no evil impulses which the mind parasite in the machine could absorb and make use of. Barnham's mind had previously been cleansed of all evil by the parasite.

13. The TOMTIT machine (and, of course, the Master's TARDIS!).

14. Izlyr, who intended to repay the debt he owed the Doctor when the Time Lord had saved his life.

15. He was forced to go into hiding to escape the Marshal's vengeance after he had attempted to warn Earth Council of the Overlord's evil schemes.

16. A Tyrannosaurus Rex.

17. He intended to escape using the TARDIS console and travel to the parallel world from which the Doctor had come.

18. Elizabeth Shaw in the parallel Earth visited by the Doctor. In so doing, she gave the Doctor the opportunity to return to *his* Earth and save it.

19. Chin Lee, the Chinese Security Chief, who under the Master's control, attempted to wreck the peace conference's chances of success.
20. A concept of time which holds that time is not 'flat', but composed of innumerable individual particles. The TOMTIT machine was able to push objects between these particles, through what Sergeant Benton eloquently described as 'the gap between now and now'.

Adventures in History/4 – page 54

1. She attempted to persuade the Aztecs to give up the barbaric practice of human sacrifice. She, of course, failed.
2. The Greeks and the Trojans involved in the Trojan War, and, of course, the TARDIS crew.
3. Professor Warlock.
4. The costumes they had worn at the Cranleigh's fancy dress ball and a copy of the book, *Black Orchid*, written by George Cranleigh.
5. The *Rocket*, the very first steam engine.
6. They used a wheel and pulley system. They took the wheel with them in order not to alter the course of history: despite their great achievements the Aztecs had not discovered the wheel.
7. Polly and Kirsty had previously captured the handsome young lieutenant and had taken a lock of his hair. Afraid that Polly could use this damning piece of evidence to prove to his fellow officers that he had been captured by two mere girls, Algernon was only too willing to offer the travellers safe passage!
8. To avenge the murder of their brother, Reuben, who had been killed by Doc Holliday.
9. The materialisation of the TARDIS so distracted Hector that Achilles was able to deliver the Trojan his death blow.
10. Ian, claiming that the Doctor was a Saracen spy, took him into the cover of the forest to 'execute' him and the two travellers gleefully escaped with Barbara and Vicki in the TARDIS.

11. Shang-Tu. The Khan's court, however, was situated in Peking.
12. Diomede (or Steven as he really was) allowed Paris to defeat him in battle. He then suggested that, rather than killing his opponent, Paris should take him into Troy to prove his skill in combat to his fellow Trojans.
13. The Doctor. He procured the uniform of Senior Citizen by trading his own clothes and his Roman ring.
14. Sutekh held back the explosion by the sheer force of his will.
15. Fatima, one of Barbara's fellow prisoners in the harem.
16. They were taken back by the Doctor in the TARDIS.
17. The Venerable Bede.
18. Aeneas and his fellows. Vicki and Troilus then went with Aeneas to build a new Troy.
19. A normal footprint whose increased size was due to the melting of the snow.
20. *Time-Flight* (140 million years in the past; some of the action of this story, however, took place in 1981); *The Time Meddler* (1066); *The Visitation* (1666); *Timelash* (1888); *Pyramids of Mars* (1911); *The Awakening* (1984; this story however had very close links with 1623, and the Doctor would later return Will Chandler to this year).

The Adventures of the Fourth Doctor/4 - page 55

1. An electrically charged sword, the power pack of which was to be found in the sword hilt. The peasants on Tara also made use of crossbows which fired electronic bolts.
2. His time-machine which was capable of accelerating time could transform, for example, an egg into a chicken in seconds.
3. Miners, most of whom lived in Megropolis Three on Pluto. The Doctor was forced to impersonate an Ajack on Pluto.
4. For the simple reason that they did not know how to operate the ship's flight controls.
5. The manservant of the Duke of Forgill.
6. The Sword of Sacrifice.

7. Tritium crystals.
8. She hoped to use the lure of regeneration made possible by Hardin's experiments in time to attract many more visitors to the Leisure Hive.
9. A sub-atomic particle which is capable of travelling faster than light.
10. Adric in *Warrior's Gate*.
11. They had become victims of Styre's experiments on Humans, done in order to ascertain humanity's potential resistance to a Sontaran invasion.
12. He needed his body as a pliable base on which to model the form of the Doctor.
13. Mensch.
14. It was originally a hydrogen reactor.
15. Princess Strella.
16. Zilda and Chub.
17. Silent gas dirigibles (see *The Brain of Morbius*).
18. The head of the British Institute of Druid Studies at Boscombe Moor. Dabbling in things he did not understand he became a servant of the Cailleach (Vivien Fay). He was killed by an Ogri.
19. The Watcher, the interim stage between the Doctor's fourth and fifth incarnations.
20. 'Light the blue touch paper and stand back'. The Doctor's gifts were two fireworks – a Mighty Atom and a Thunderclap.

The Adventures of the Fifth Doctor/4 – page 56

1. Five hundred years.
2. A showman on Manussa who was possessed by the Mara.
3. The brand of a Trion criminal. To the people of Sarn it was the mark of the Chosen One. Malkon and Turlough both carried the Misos Triangle on their arms.
4. Sharaz Jek.
5. The white TARDIS hat-stand which contained some residual energy from the 'destroyed' time-machine.
6. By the Doctor's possession of a sonic screwdriver and his knowledge of soliton gas and Terileptil technology;

and also by the clothes worn by Tegan and Adric which were made of a fibre unknown to seventeenth-century Earth. (Strictly speaking, of course, Tegan was not an alien, although she did come from the Earth of three centuries later.) Tegan tried to persuade the Terileptil that the Doctor did, in fact, come from Guildford. She met with little success ...

7. Proton missiles.
8. Timanov. The god was, in reality, a Trion vulcanologist dressed in a protective suit.
9. He hoped that they would keep him company in his underground lair. He desired Peri's great beauty and valued the intellectual stimulation which the Doctor could provide him.
10. Adric, the Melkur and a Terileptil. Adric's wearing his gold star for mathematical excellence convinced the girls that he was an illusion, as the badge had been shattered when the Doctor destroyed the Cyberleader on board the TARDIS.
11. (a) Total Survival Suit; (b) Intelligent Life Form; (c) Zone of Maximum Impact; (d) Total Area of Destruction.
12. He successfully blocked the transfer of psychic energy which was being directed at the Malus by its parent image in Little Hodcombe church.
13. The general who trained both Olvir and Valgard in combat fighting.
14. Ruther; Mergrave; Shardovan; the Portreeve (the Master).
15. Scibus and Tarpok.
16. 1984 at Little Hodcombe. The battles were, in fact, war games recreating the battle of 1643.
17. Doctor Runciman.
18. The daughter of Mr Range on Frontios who helped the TARDIS crew. She was briefly captured by the Tractators.
19. Sauvix.
20. His body was used in, and exhausted by, the Tractators' excavating machine.

1. They intended to ensure that the Cyber Planet of Mondas was not destroyed in 1986, by destroying the Earth itself.

2. Eric Klieg.

3. Gold is the perfect non-corrodable metal and plates the Cybermen's breathing apparatus.

4. To investigate the massacre (by the Cyber Androids) of seven of her party, of which she was the only survivor. Other named members of Scott's party were Walters, Mitchell and Snyder.

5. The Cyber Director on Earth at the time of the Cybermen's invasion of that planet.

6. In *Tomb of the Cybermen* and *Attack of the Cybermen*.

7. The Doctor proposed that they wait until Mondas destroyed itself by absorbing too much energy from its sister planet.

8. Berger.

9. Toberman, the manservant of Kaftan.

10. He managed to jam the Cybermen's signal which would have detonated the bomb, and then deactivated the device.

11. Flast, echoing a feeling shared by her fellow Cryons. Upon leaving the planet, the Cybermen intended to destroy it.

12. Professor Parry's archaeological team. The Cybermen had logically deduced that intelligent creatures would one day penetrate their stronghold – creatures which would be suitable for transformation into Cybermen.

13. To use Captain Brigg's freighter as a guided missile.

14. By Flast igniting the Cybermen's stock of vaskil with the sonic lance given to her by the Doctor. Flast was killed by the Cybermen who exposed her to warm air, but the sonic lance remained undetected.

15. They proposed to divert the course of Halley's Comet and crash it into the Earth. Halley's Comet made its regular appearance in 1986, the year in which Mondas was destroyed.

1. The mark left on the jugular vein of any human upon whom the Rani had operated to extract their valuable brain fluid. It also provided the Rani with some control over that person's actions.
2. Necros.
3. Sil.
4. Its fishing.
5. The beautiful and ruthless head of a protein refinery company on Necros. She planned to win great power by controlling the food supplies for the entire galaxy and, in so doing, played a deadly game with Davros, on whom she relied for supplies of protein.
6. Kara's secretary on Necros, of whom she seemed to be particularly fond. He was exterminated by Davros's Daleks.
7. Azmael.
8. During his third incarnation, when he presented Katz's grandfather with a locket containing the photograph of Jo Grant.
9. George Stephenson's sponsor who helped the sixth Doctor and Peri on nineteenth-century Earth.
10. The *herbum bacillae vitae*, or staff of life, a violet flower particularly abundant on Necros and similar to the soya bean plant on Earth. When refined it is an excellent source of protein.
11. She intended to use them to destroy her Sontaran allies.
12. They needed his help to ensure that the Cybermen would never use their stolen time-ship to leave Telos, and destroy Earth.
13. The widow of the Dom Vincente Arana who lived alone in the hacienda which was occupied by Chessene and the Sontarans. Blind and devoted to her religion, she was killed by Shockeye and her mind drained of knowledge by Chessene.
14. He was chosen by lot among the twelve most senior officer guards on Varos.
15. They were sentenced to the Timelash.
16. He was needed to prime the Kartz and Reimer time-capsule and thereby make it capable of time-travel.

17. He intended that the prisoners' escape should distract Davros's guards, thereby enabling him to kill the evil Kaled.
18. Two average Varosians who took great delight in watching the tortures inflicted upon the Doctor and his friends in the Punishment Dome. Etta supported the current Governor's policies while Arak longed for a new Governor. When the Varosians' barbaric system of torture and slavery was ended they were faced with an uncertain future.
19. H.G. Wells.
20. To use the power of time-travel to lead her fellow Androguns to power throughout the Universe.

The Adventures of the First Doctor/5 – page 59

1. They held Steven hostage.
2. The head of International Space Command in Geneva. He was killed by the Cybermen from Mondas.
3. The spearhead of the Menoptera invasion force.
4. The costume consisted of ceremonial robes and a mask used by the Didonians. The jewelled club, which Bennett used as a weapon, was, in fact, a Didonian tool employed in construction work.
5. When the TARDIS jumped a time track they saw a vision of themselves as exhibits in the Moroks' Space Museum – their fate if they could not defeat the invaders of Xeros.
6. Avon and Flower.
7. Four.
8. He was wary of the teachers' revealing the existence of himself and Susan; and he also lacked the necessary data to calculate a course home from prehistoric Earth.
9. It fed itself on the vegetation and minerals supplied to it by its slave workers, and gained in strength, spreading its malign presence all over Vortis.
10. A black marketeer who took advantage of the misery and poverty of the Humans at the Dalek mines in Bedfordshire. He fell victim to the Daleks' Slyther.
11. Major Green. He was taken over by WOTAN.

12. Za.
13. They planned to throw them down into the fire chasms of their planet.
14. The arrival of the TARDIS.
15. On the banks of the Thames in twenty-second-century London which had been taken over by the Daleks.
16. They burnt off the Menoptera's wings.
17. Paris.
18. He checked the Astral Map in the TARDIS.
19. The daughter of the Commander of the Space Ark who spoke in the Doctor's defence during the Time Lord's visit to the Ark.
20. No. However, in the pilot episode of *An Unearthly Child*, which was never broadcast, Susan reveals that her grandfather and herself came from the forty-ninth century.

The Adventures of the Fourth Doctor/5 – page 61

1. Startled at the appearance of the hideous form of a Jagaroth inside Professor Kerensky's time-machine, Hermann, Scarlioni's henchman, threw a batch of inflammable chemicals at Scaroth, which resulted in a fire and the destruction of both Scaroth and the time-machine. The fire also destroyed six of the seven Mona Lisas painted by da Vinci – including the only one on which the Doctor had not written *This is a fake* in felt tip pen!
2. The Nimon.
3. Andor; Calib; Sole; Tomas; Neeva; Leela; Lugo.
4. He planned to use his android double as a diversion to distract the attention of Count Grendel's hired assassin, during which time, the real Prince could be smuggled safely into the coronation room and claim his rightful inheritance as King of Tara.
5. He truly died when he entered Sutekh's tomb in Egypt. His body was destroyed on Mars after he had destroyed the Eye of Horus.
6. Because he was unable to pay the excessive taxes imposed on him by the Company.

7. Desperately wanting to communicate with the Chlorissans in the only way he knew how – by physical contact – he crushed his victims to death.
8. He imprisoned the two Gallifreyans in a Time Loop. They broke the loop by throwing out of phase the actions they were forced to repeatedly perform – by performing them a few seconds earlier than they were forced to.
9. Adric.
10. The Doctor and Romana were obliged to use two of the crystals to give the cruiser enough power to break free of the Black Hole into which it was being drawn.
11. Sarah was given a pass by the Brigadier, and Harry posed as a Ministry of Health inspector.
12. Drax, whom the Doctor met in the Class of '93. Drax was thrown out of the Academy because of his inability to handle temporal theory.
13. He claimed he only needed the money to fund his scientific research.
14. Space.
15. Bandits who threatened Romana and the Doctor on Chloris. They were originally miners who turned to crime when the Lady Adrasta closed down the mines.
16. From their punt on the River Cam.
17. Loch Ness.
18. Morix. Mena was his consort and took over from him on his death.
19. In the Undercity beneath Megropolis One.
20. They died when the Great Vampire, who had unnaturally extended their lives, was destroyed by the Doctor.

The Adventures of the Fifth Doctor/5 – page 62

1. General Chellak's every move was reported to Sharaz Jek by his android double of Major Salateen who had infiltrated Chellak's base.
2. He made use of the momentum generated by throwing a cricket ball at the side of Monarch's ship to propel himself through space to the security of the TARDIS.

3. While purporting to be over five hundred years old, the books detailed the history of Castrovalva up to the present day – evidence that Castrovalva had in fact been created by the Master, using Adric's mathematical abilities.

4. Two young men of Sarn who dared to climb the Fire Mountain to find that the god Logar was but a myth.

5. He feared that his presence on Frontios would dramatically influence the new colony's future. He was obliged to land there when the Tractators' gravitational powers dragged the TARDIS down to the planet's surface.

6. Hippo was the nickname of Ibbotson, one of Turlough's schoolfriends at Brendon. A fat and uninteresting boy, he seemed to be rather in awe of his companion.

7. In the crypt of Little Hodcombe church.

8. He pumped hexachromite gas into the Sea Base's ventilation system – with great reluctance. Hexachromite is an underwater sealing agent which is lethal to marine and reptile life.

9. The energy released when the Brigadier of 1977 came face to face with his counterpart from 1983 at the very moment when the Doctor's 'life force' was to be transmitted to Mawdryn and his fellow scientists.

10. He simply walked past them. Jek's androids were programmed only to attack Humans – and the Doctor is not a Human.

11. They made use of their bodies to power their Excavating Machine.

12. Deva Loka.

13. Sketches provided by Tegan. It was necessary for the Urbankans to appear human to the Earthpeople so as not to frighten them.

14. *The Five Doctors*. Tegan, of course, doubted whether the changes were for the better.

15. The amiable farmer met by the TARDIS crew in Little Hodcombe. He took an active part in Sir George Hutchinson's war games, until he realised the direction they were taking, and helped the Doctor in his battle with the Malus.

16. With control bracelets.

17. The solar generator panels of the Dome.
18. She had made a vow that she would remain silent until she was reunited with her own people.
19. A mysterious and probably fifth-dimensional energy which in some way seems to power the TARDIS. The fifth Doctor admitted to Monarch that he really did not understand the exact nature of this energy, and certainly Monarch's computer had no records whatsoever of any such energy.
20. He was killed by a shot from Stotz's gun as Jek fought Morgus in a battle to the death. Stotz was then killed by Jek's faithful android, his Salateen replica.

Companions of the Doctor/4 – page 63

1. He was destroyed – at his own request – by the Doctor who used the Master's Tissue Compression Eliminator.
2. She had taken a temporary leave of absence from the TARDIS to study graphology.
3. Sarah Jane.
4. *The Celestial Toymaker*. The King and Queen were, of course, the King and Queen of Hearts.
5. Leela by Mr Sin, the Peking Homunculus.
6. 7 June 1977, the official day of celebration in honour of the silver jubilee of Queen Elizabeth II.
7. Professor Litefoot in nineteenth-century England.
8. Zoe.
9. Barbara by Nero.
10. A dog whistle.
11. In the dream she experienced on Deva Loka. She also saw her possessed self in a mirror on Manussa. Both times she was under the influence of the Mara.
12. Leela. Her primitive emotions suited her better outside the Capitol where she would also pose less of a threat to his plans.
13. Malkon. The rest of his family were killed when their spacecraft crashlanded on Sarn.
14. Dodo in the Wild West.
15. (a) Turlough; (b) Nyssa; (c) Romana.

1. He intended to use the mathematical abilities of the Sylvest twins to alter the orbits of Jaconda's two neighbouring planets in such a way that they would crash into their sun, thereby creating a supernova, the force of which would propel Mestor's eggs throughout the Universe. Mestor's claim that he planned to move the planets closer to Jaconda so as to facilitate their farming was a ruse designed to ensure Azmael's co-operation.

2. The Sontarans chose Earth because it was conveniently situated for them to launch an attack on the Rutans in the Madillon Cluster. Chessene chose Earth to please Shockeye who had a strong desire to taste human flesh. She too was more than a little curious about the flavour of the human animal.

3. The invasion force changed its course to the asteroid Biosculptor when great quantities of Zeiton 7 ore were detected there. So precious was the ore to Sil's company that he was then instructed to offer the Varosians whatever they asked for the ore.

4. That the Doctor return his medal to the Grand Order of Oberon and tell them that he died an honourable death.

5. Luke Ward, or rather the tree into which he had been transformed and which still held some vestiges of his humanity.

6. Payne, Russel and Griffiths.

7. He used the TARDIS as a deflector shield, and successfully detonated the missile in Karfel's stratosphere.

8. He followed the Doctor's blood trail.

9. One of the twelve most senior guard officers on Varos who had come to that position on the Governor's accession to his post. Initially faithful to the Varosian system of government, he later saw the error of his ways.

10. By feeding them with specially inpregnated maggot-like creatures.

11. Bostock.

12. Unlimited time-travel. The Sontarans do possess a limited time-travel facility, as was seen when Linx

transported twentieth-century scientists to the Middle Ages, but unlimited time-travel as possessed by the Time Lords has been one of their most sought-after goals, which even led them to an invasion attempt on Gallifrey.

13. Placed together with a similar amulet it formed the key to the Borad's power vaults.

14. She was killed by Orcini.

15. He suggested that the Weed Plant of Necros be refined into protein to satisfy that part of the galaxy's great need for food.

16. Kontron Crytals have a wide application of uses. The Doctor used one on Karfel to time-slip ten seconds, and to project an image of himself. He also used it on the Borad and absorbed the dictator's time acceleration beam, passed it through a ten second time loop and reflected it back on his enemy.

17. He 'moth-balled' him with cyanide which he found in Oscar Botcherby's butterfly jar.

18. When his mind was taken over by Mestor, the Time Lord, who had reached the end of his cycle of regeneratons, forced himself to regenerate – in effect, willed himself to death. Mestor was unable to return to his own body which the Doctor had destroyed with acid.

19. The Rani's operations on the men to extract their precious brain fluid had also robbed them of the power to sleep, and thus accounted for their violent and restless behaviour.

20. Those who opposed the Borad's rule included: Aram, Tyheer, Gazak, Sezon, Katz, Vena, Mykros. Vena's father, Renis, was also opposed to the Borad, but died before he could take any positive action against the evil dictator.

General/3 – page 65

1. (a) Solos; (b) Varos; (c) Mars and Peladon; (d) Voga; (e) Telos.

2. A 'time corridor in space'. One was constructed by the Timelash.

3. In *The Two Doctors* when the sixth Doctor tracked

down his second incarnation in Seville.

4. (i) that it was destroyed in the devastation caused by the Doctor's defeat of Professor Zaroff's plans; (ii) that it was destroyed by the Daemons; (iii) that it was destroyed by the wrath of Kronos.

5. (a) A professor from Darlington University who sacrificed himself to the Xeraphin; (b) Peri's step-father whose form Kamelion briefly assumed; (c) The alias of Salyavin, the Time Lord, and one of the Doctor's heroes. He was living in Cambridge when the Doctor and Romana met him in *Shada*.

6. In *Planet of Giants* with the other members of the TARDIS crew; in *The Armageddon Factor* as part of his attempt to thwart the plans of the Shadow; and in *Logopolis* when he fell victim to one of the Master's traps. Professor Marius also introduced a minituarised clone of the Doctor into the Time Lord's body in *The Invisible Enemy*.

7. (a) *The Curse of Peladon*; (b) *The Gunfighters*; (c) *Enemy of the World*; (d) *The Face of Evil*.

8. He journeyed there during the Dalek's Master Plan, and also during Sutekh's attempts to break free of his prison.

9. (a) talmar; (b) opek.

10. The Daleks.

11. Mondas, the Cybermen's home planet.

12. Being Earth's twin planet, the land masses of Mondas were extremely similar to those on Earth.

13. (a) the Animus; (b) the Gravis; (c) the Great Intelligence.

14. *Invasion of Time*.

15. *The War Machines*.

The Daleks and the Thals/4 – page 66

1. By placing his duplicates in influential and strategic positions throughout the globe. The fifth Doctor was sure that, given time, the duplicates would free themselves from Dalek conditioning, basing his assumption on the actions of Stien.

2. Takis and Lilt on Necros.

3. His appearance did not tally with their records of their

136

arch-enemy, despite Davros's insistence that the Doctor
had regenerated. They intended to hold the Time Lord
prisoner until his identity could be confirmed.

4. Genocide.
5. Stien, who, exterminated by Daleks, activated the space
   station's self-destruct system in his dying moments.
6. The scientist in Colonel Archer's bomb disposal squad.
   She befriended Tegan, but was killed by Archer's
   duplicated soldiers.
7. Sara Kingdom.
8. Artificial sunlight.
9. He planned to record his warning on tape and then eject
   it into orbit where it would transmit its message to
   listening posts throughout the galaxy. Cory was unable
   to launch the beacon which was to carry the recording
   into orbit, but the tape was found by the Doctor,
   together with Cory's skeleton, some months later.
10. The body of the Daleks' creator, Davros.
11. The Daleks' spacecraft and the first floor of a warehouse
    in twentieth-century London.
12. The Daleks' clearing by flame of the jungle on Kembel to
    destroy any opposition to their plans.
13. A Time Corridor; and Stien. Stien proved to be the more
    effective trap.
14. They needed the Doctor and his brainwaves to construct
    a duplicate of the Time Lord to infiltrate and murder
    the High Council on Gallifrey.
15. He used an escape pod which he had prepared. He was
    then fortuitously picked up by a space transporter and
    taken to Necros.

The Adventures of the Fifth Doctor/6 – page 67

1. Because they were convicted criminals who had escaped
   from the prison planet of Raaga.
2. Morgus.
3. They believed them to be missiles fired at Frontios from
   a neighbouring and hostile planet.
4. The rocks were drawn from a neighbouring asteroid belt
   by the Tractators' gravitational powers, in their plans to

capture Humans to establish a slave colony.

5. He was taken back by the Doctor in the TARDIS.
6. Two identical androids, constructed by Sharaz Jek, took their places.
7. The Doctor, who set the TARDIS's co-ordinates following Tegan's instructions. Tegan had, of course, been taken over by the Mara.
8. The headmaster.
9. With ultra-violet light.
10. The Black and the White Guardian.
11. A helmet dating back to the middle Sumaran era on Manussa and consisting of five faces. The sixth face – the face of the helmet's wearer – was the sixth Face of Delusion.
12. Psychic energy.
13. He introduced a homing device into the capsule's circuitry and homed in onto the TARDIS which was on board Monarch's ship.
14. With the rum which the crewmembers were supplied with.
15. The site of the crashed Trion spacecraft, among the wreckage of which Malkon was found and hailed as the Chosen One.
16. Wilson persuaded Vorshak to hand over a duplicate programme disc, with which he and Solav could reprogramme Haddox so that he would obey only their commands.
17. The captain of Speedbird Concorde 192 which vanished down a time contour en route to Heathrow from New York and materialised on the Earth of 140 million years ago.
18. Random particles of protein assembled from the atmosphere by the Master's skill at psychokinesis.
19. The TARDIS would offer the freedom to move between the planets which the Gravis so desperately desired.
20. A deadly poisoning, contracted by contact with spectrox in its raw unrefined state. It is usually fatal. The only known cure is the milk of the Queen Bat, which lives in the lower reaches of the caves of Androzani Minor. Both the Doctor and Peri contracted spectrox poisoning; Peri was cured by the antidote, and the

Doctor, having no antidote left, regenerated to save his life.

The Adventures of the Sixth Doctor/6 – page 68

1. A villainess and a 'woman of rare guile and devilish cunning'. She was certainly known to the second and sixth Doctors, although any meeting they may have had is not recorded.
2. Mortally wounded by coronic acid, he vapourised himself and his spacecraft on twentieth-century Earth.
3. In the Tombs of the Cybermen.
4. He banished the Borad to the vicinity of Inverness in the year 1179 by using the Timelash.
5. Bostock, Orcini's squire.
6. To control her alien subjects on Miasimia Goria she needed a certain chemical which was to be found only in the human brain.
7. The technical advisor and controller of all that happened in the Punishment Dome on Varos – in other words, a torturer.
8. He died after having come in contact with a poisoned barb in the Punishment Dome.
9. Those of superior intellect he turned into Daleks; the rest he intended to refine down into protein which would be used as a food substitute.
10. Flast.
11. A deadly section of the Punishment Dome on Varos in which prisoners were subjected to terrifying hallucinations.
12. The son of Jack Ward, a protogee of Lord Ravensworth and the assistant to George Stephenson. His brilliant career was abruptly curtailed when one of the Rani's deadly 'mines' transformed him into a tree in Redfern Dell.
13. Chemistry.
14. Two scientists researching into time-travel on Dastari's space station.
15. He used the key to his own TARDIS.
16. Flast, Varne, Rost and Threst.

17. The Chief Officer.
18. The Cybermen.
19. Renis.
20. Davros.

Behind the Scenes/2 – page 69

1. (a) Richard Martin; (b) Douglas Camfield; (c) Christopher Barry; (d) Peter Grimwade; (e) Graeme Harper; (f) Graeme Harper.
2. Peter Grimwade, who wrote *Planet of Fire, Mawdryn Undead* and *Time-Flight*.
3. In both cases, the Master. The actor, Neil Toynay (an anagram of Tony Ainley) played the role of the Portreeve (the Master) in *Castrovalva*, and James Stoker (an anagram of Master's Joke) played Gilles Estram (also an alias of the Master) in *The King's Demons*.
4. The first story to be repeated was *Evil of the Daleks*. However, the episode, *An Unearthly Child*, was also repeated a week after its first screening.
5. (a) Eric Saward; (b) Louis Marks; (c) David Whitaker; (d) Terry Nation and Dennis Spooner.
6. The producer of the two Dalek films in the 1960s.
7. *The War Machines*.
8. (a) The first Doctor in *The Five Doctors*; (b) the second incarnation of Romana; (c) the Rani; (d) Borusa in *The Five Doctors*; (e) the Meddling Monk.
9. In, respectively, *Doctor Who and the Daleks* and *Daleks: Invasion Earth 2150 AD*, the two Dalek films.
10. Jenny in the stage play *Doctor Who and the Seven Keys to Doomsday*.
11. A record album, released by Argo records, and featuring Tom Baker and Elisabeth Sladen.
12. Ian Marter – Harry Sullivan; William Russell – Ian Chesterton; Matthew Waterhouse – Adric; Peter Purves – Steven Taylor.
13. Hilio in *The Web Planet*; Butler in *Invasion of the Dinosaurs*; and the Governor in *Vengeance on Varos*.
14. John Levene who played Sergeant Benton.

15. Jack and Debbie Watling were father and daughter.
16. *City of Death*, set in Paris; *Arc of Infinity* in Amsterdam; *Planet of Fire* in Lanzarote; and *The Two Doctors* in Seville.
17. A proposed film project which was to feature Tom Baker as the the Doctor in battle with Vincent Price.
18. Mavic Chen and Tobias Vaughn.
19. *The Ark in Space* and *Revenge of the Cybermen*, both of which were set on Nerva.
20. Colin Baker as Paul Merroney in *The Brothers*.